PRESERVE
PROTECT
&DEFEND

CAMERON C. TAYLOR

Other Books by Cameron C. Taylor

Does Your Bag Have Holes?
24 Truths That Lead to Financial and Spiritual Freedom

8 Attributes of Great Achievers

Twelve Paradoxes of the Gospel

Author Websites

www.DoesYourBagHaveHoles.org
www.TheGloriousCauseOfAmerica.org

This book is dedicated to GeorgeWashington.

"Cameron has created a work that transcends all others. He beautifully merges history, truth, and an edge of your seat thriller into a book that you cannot put down. *Preserve, Protect and Defend* is one of the best written narratives in the world. I highly recommend this book."

- Dale West
President of West & West Accounting

"The book *Preserve, Protect and Defend* is amazing! I couldn't stop reading! The suspense and reality of the events that are taking place make you feel like you are right there in the action. The chapters where Vice President Banner is learning at the feet of our Founding Fathers is truly inspiring. I felt like I was there in heaven, learning from the inspired men that followed the Holy Spirit as they framed the Declaration of Independence and Constitution. Thank you Cameron! I will share this book with everyone I know."

- Tom Sathre
Gandolfo's Deli Owner

"The book *Preserve, Protect and Defend* is one you will not want to put down! Cameron has done an excellent job weaving the story so you want more and more and don't want it to end! He also addresses something that is precious that is quickly becoming lost. We must fight for freedom."

- Barbara Munson
Executive Assistant

"Cameron has done an amazing thing. He has given the reader the excitement of enjoying a great novel while at the same time teaching the reader the specific constitutional principles the American Founders believed would make this country great. I highly recommend it to Americans everywhere."

- G. Kent Mangelson
President of Wealth of America, Inc.

Table of Contents

PREFACE

I have written several books over the past five years and felt it was time to write another. Over the years, I have kept a file of future book ideas and I began to ponder what I should write about next. I started working on several different books; however, none of them felt like the book I was supposed to be writing. During this time, I received recommendations by three different people within two weeks to read a particular book that I had never heard of before. I got the message that I needed to read this book. I ordered the book and read through it in a couple of days. The book used a fictional character and story to teach various principles.

After finishing the book, I had the impression that I needed to write a similar style of book, where true principles were taught through a fictional story. When I told my wife that I was going to write a novelesque book she quipped, "How do you plan on writing a novel when you have never even read a novel?" I replied, "If God wants me to write a novel, I can write a novel." She responded, "If you write a novel, it will definitely increase my belief in miracles." Well, the book you are about to read is a miracle. When I started writing, it was clear to me that this was the book I was supposed to be writing.

When my book *Does Your Bag Have Holes?* was first released, I had my staff provide a complimentary copy to each of the postal workers who were shipping orders for the book across the country. One day while at the post office I handed the clerk my credit card to pay and he looked at the name on the card and said, "Hey, you're the author of the book *Does Your Bag Have Holes?*" He then looked at me somewhat perplexed and asked, "Did you really write that book?" I replied, "Yes. I would be considered the author of the book." Having a hard time believing I was the author, he again looked at the name Cameron C. Taylor on the credit card and then looked at me and said, "You couldn't have written that book. It is really good." His comment brought a smile to my face and I said, "I'll take that as a great compliment, because while I was the one to put words on the page, I give all honor and praise for the book to God. I was merely an instrument in His hands." The postal worker then replied, "That makes sense. I knew you had to have help."

Philo T. Farnsworth, the inventor of television, wrote, "I know that God exists. I know that I have never invented anything. I have been a medium by which these things were given to the culture as fast as the culture could earn them. I give all the credit to God."[1] I echo his words. I have never created a book. I give all the credit to God.

I love reading and writing about the founding of America and the Founding Fathers. A great spirit resonates with the founders and the history of The United States of America. I am grateful for their sacrifice, dedication, and integrity.

The Revolutionary War was one of the longest wars in our history, lasting eight and a half years. One percent of the population sacrificed their lives in the glorious cause of America. "If we were to fight for our independence today and the war was equally costly, there would be more than three million of us killed."[2] Abigail Adams wrote in a letter to her husband John in 1777, "Posterity who are to reap the blessings, will scarcely be able to conceive the hardships and sufferings of their ancestors."[3]

As one of the blessed recipients of freedom, this book has helped me to better understand those who fought and suffered to establish a new independent nation, and the principles they put into the US Constitution to establish and protect freedom. As the blessed recipients of freedom, we must ensure that their sacrifices and principles are not forgotten and freedom is not lost. Enjoy the book!

Cameron C. Taylor

PRESERVE, PROTECT & DEFEND

CHAPTER 1:
COMMENCEMENT

"Any last minutes changes you would like to make to your speech, Mr. Vice President?"

Aaron Banner smiled at his assistant and answered, "No changes. Thank you." He had spent half the night memorizing his speech. He had never been very comfortable with teleprompters, and reading a speech made it harder for him to really connect with his audience, so he did his best to deliver the speech from memory and from the heart.

Aaron asked for a few minutes to be alone. Moments of solitude were usually brief due to his full schedule and being constantly surrounded with staff. Once alone, he went over his presentation notes one final time, then knelt and prayed for the Lord to strengthen and guide his words. As he was completing his prayer, there was a knock at the door and the voice of his assistant saying, "Mr. Vice President, it's time."

Forty thousand people were gathered at Stanford Stadium for

the 131st commencement ceremony. It was a nice sunny day with a beautiful clear blue sky. Sounds of chatter echoed through the stadium as the crowd waited for the ceremonies to begin.

Vice President Banner came through one of the stadium tunnels and walked toward the large stage that had been assembled on the football field for the occasion. The audience, seeing his entrance, rose to their feet and stood in silence. By the time Aaron reached his seat, most of the crowd was standing, watching him silently. As he took his seat, a member of the crowd pierced the silence and shouted, "We love you." A large smile filled Vice President Banner's face, as a chuckle rippled through the crowd; he then signaled with his hands for the audience to be seated.

Stanford's eleventh President, John L. Henry, took the podium to begin the commencement saying, "On my way to the stadium today I walked past a mother taking a picture of her graduating son with his father. I overheard the mother say, 'Let's try to make this look natural—put your arm around your dad's shoulder.' The father retorted, 'If you want it to look natural, why not have him put his hand in my pocket?'"

President Henry paused to let the laughter take its course and then continued, "Your families are extremely proud of you today. You cannot imagine the sense of relief they are experiencing, knowing they will not have to write another check to Stanford University." A roar of approval from the audience greeted this comment. President Henry waited for the cheering to subside and continued, "Since I know you did not come today to hear me speak, I will be brief in my introduction of our keynote speaker. We are honored today to hear from a public servant, advocate of freedom, philanthropist, man of faith, and fiftieth Vice President of the United States, Aaron W. Banner!"

Thunderous applause filled the stadium as Vice President Banner rose to take the podium. As President Henry and Vice President Banner crossed paths they firmly shook one another's hands. The noise of the crowd covered the sincere thanks Vice President Banner gave to Stanford's President for his introduction. President Henry put his arm on Vice President Banner's shoulder as they stood together momentarily, conscious of the snapping cameras capturing the moment.

President Henry took his seat as Vice President Banner stepped in front of the microphone. Aaron waved and smiled as he waited for the clapping and cheering to subside. After a few moments, a hush fell over the entire stadium, as the audience anticipated his first words.

He began, "It is an honor to be invited to speak to you today. Each of you in this audience—graduating students, parents, friends, siblings—each and every one of you has been given special gifts and talents from God which only you possess. To quote Victor Frankl, 'Everyone has his own specific vocation or mission in life to carry out a concrete assignment which demands fulfillment. Therein he cannot be replaced, nor can his life be repeated. Thus, everyone's task is as unique as is his specific opportunity to implement it.'[4] Preachers are here to minister to our souls; doctors to heal our diseases; teachers to open up our . . ."

His next words were lost as the sound of gunfire echoed viciously through the stadium. Shouts of fear and anxiety permeated the crowd as they frantically sought to find cover. Rapid shots seemed to be coming from every direction. The lead Secret Service agent was behind the

Vice President on the stage, and to his view, everything seemed to be happening in slow motion. As he sprinted toward the Vice President, he saw the Vice President's body jolt to the left as a bullet hit him from the right and his body then jolted to the right as he was hit by another bullet from the left. Several more shots were fired in quick succession as the Vice President's body folded over and began falling to the floor.

The agent continued his lunge in an attempt to catch the falling Vice President and cover him from further fire, but it had all occurred so quickly, and he was unable to reach him in time. He watched in horror as the Vice President fell to the ground. Vice President Banner's head was first to hit and absorbed the full brunt of the fall. His body soon followed, hitting the floor awkwardly.

The agent quickly secured himself as a human shield over the wounded Vice President to protect him from further harm, but the sound of gunfire had ceased. Other agents gathered with their weapons drawn, encircling the Vice President's body as he lay unconscious on the platform. The rest were searching for the source of the shots and radioing university and city police for assistance in apprehending the assassins. There were times the Vice President wore a bulletproof vest, but today was not one of them.

An ambulance, prepositioned at the stadium for the commencement ceremonies, was quickly brought onto the field as closely to the raised platform as possible. Aaron Banner's limp body was quickly secured onto the stretcher and placed inside the ambulance. As they attended to him in the ambulance, he remained unconscious.

Stanford Hospital was less than two miles away and the ambulance sped through traffic with the siren blaring, hoping to get him medical attention in time to save his life. Calls to the hospital had been made, alerting them that the Vice President had been shot and would be arriving shortly. The medical staff quickly made the necessary preparations to be ready for his arrival. The ambulance pulled under the covered awning in front of the emergency entrances at high speed, and even before the ambulance was at a full stop, the medical staff raced to open the doors and rushed the Vice President into the emergency room.

The doctors were prepared to treat the numerous gunshot wounds that had been reported. But what the doctors found astounded them. The Vice President had multiple bullet holes through his clothing, but there was not one scratch on his body.

The Vice President lay unconscious on the operating room gurney, but his heart rate, blood pressure, and oxygen levels were all reading at normal levels on the monitors. He was taken from the operating room for an MRI to see what head trauma he had suffered. As the doctors reviewed the images, no trauma to the head or brain was detected, but there was a large bump and bruise forming where his head had hit the ground.

CHAPTER 2:
MEETING IN HEAVEN

Vice President Banner awoke to find himself in a large room. The room was filled with a peace, warmth, light, and love that greatly surpassed any such feelings he had ever experienced before. This feeling of peace was unexpected as he had just been surrounded by complete chaos, but it was overwhelmingly strong and encircled him completely. The intense love he felt was more than he could comprehend or absorb. He could not help the tears that came to his eyes as he was enveloped in unconditional love.

An all-penetrating light, with seemingly no source, gradually filled the room, and he saw that he was sitting at a large, solid-gold conference table surrounded by very distinguished looking men.

"Where am I?" Vice President Banner asked.

The man at the head of the table replied, "You are in heaven."

Vice President Banner hesitantly questioned, "Am I dead?"

The man at the head of the table answered, "No, you are very much alive, but your body lies in a coma at Stanford Hospital."

Vice President Banner recognized the man at the head of the table from somewhere. He was sure that he'd seen him before. He had the feeling that he should know the name of this man, but he had to ask, "What is your name?"

The man smiled and answered, "My name is George Washington. I would have thought a Vice President of the United States would recognize me."

Vice President Banner froze and looked intently into the face of the man before him. Now that it was pointed out, he could see the resemblance to the paintings he was well acquainted with. He had several paintings of George Washington in his home and office. Washington was a man whose principles, policies, and attributes he sought to emulate.

"It is an honor to meet you, Mr. President," replied Vice President Banner.

George Washington responded, "Please call me George, and would it be okay for me to call you Aaron?"

"Yes, that would be fine, Mr. President, I mean George," answered Aaron. It didn't feel right being on a first name basis with the father of the nation, but if that is what he wanted, he was happy to oblige.

Aaron continued, "You mentioned that my body lies in a coma at Stanford Hospital. So am I going to die?"

"Sure you are going to die, but not anytime soon. Following our meeting, you will return to your body and find yourself in perfect health," replied Washington.

Aaron said in a perplexed voice, "How is that possible? I was shot several times. I felt the bullets hit my body."

In response, Washington shared, "With God all things are possible. When I was twenty-three years old, I was serving as a colonel in the British army during the French and Indian War. With 1,300 soldiers, we marched to take over Fort Duquesne. On the evening of July 8, 1755, we were about fifteen miles from the fort. General Braddock was the commander in charge and the officers and soldiers were in the highest spirits and firm in their conviction that they should victoriously enter the walls of Fort Duquesne. On the morning of July 9, we proceeded in perfect order along the river. One of the most beautiful spectacles I have ever beheld was the display of the British troops on this eventful morning. Every man was neatly dressed in full uniform, the soldiers were arranged in columns that stretched nearly four miles and they marched in exact order. The sun gleamed from their polished muskets and the river flowed with tranquility on our right and the deep forest overshadowed us with solemn grandeur on the left. The officers and soldiers were equally inspirited with cheering hopes and confident anticipations. "[5]

As Washington spoke, the scene began to unfold in Aaron's mind. He closed his eyes as he pictured the soldiers in their elegant red coats. He clearly saw in his mind the beauty of the morning, seeing the sunlight glinting off the river. He could even smell the freshness of the crisp forest air. He took in a deep, thoughtful breath and felt a cool breeze slide against his face and heard the sounds of rhythmic marching. He opened his eyes to find himself in an unexpected place for the second time that day. He looked around to see the lines of British soldiers marching a mere fifteen feet from where he stood. He scanned the line of marching solders, looking for the officers, who were mounted and riding smoothly among the troops. He picked out Washington easily this time, the young colonel looking calm and confident as he rode along.

Aaron then felt a hand upon his shoulder and turned to see George Washington from heaven at his side who said, "We were approximately seven miles from Fort Duquesne when the peacefulness of the morning was shattered." Aaron did not have time to ask for details before the first shots rang out. The soldiers began to fall in the front. As more shots rang out, the soldiers on the right flank began to fall. Aaron was immediately engulfed in the chaos. This was no mere exchange of bullets as enemies sized up one another in a traditional battle. This was a complete ambush. The musket fire was in quick and continued succession.

Aaron cried out, feeling helpless as more and more soldiers fell to the ground in the chaos. The fresh smell of the air was replaced by the heavy scent of smoke and gunpowder. The beauty of the day was gone as the scene of the dead and the dying quickly took its place. The ground was stained crimson and covered with hundreds of the dying and the dead.

Aaron watched as the officers became clear targets of the enemy and were shot from their horses. Horses thrashed about as they too were targeted and shot out from under their riders. The British soldiers tried valiantly to fight back, firing their weapons into the trees, but their enemies were hidden and all but invisible in the cover of the forest.

As Aaron looked on, a riderless horse tore along the road, wounded and frenzied. It pulled a wagon after it, dragging it over both the living and the dead.[6] He then saw that only one man remained on horseback. He was an obvious and important target as he moved about, commanding and encouraging the soldiers. It was the young Colonel Washington, and as he was shouting commands, his horse was shot. As it fell to the ground, Washington leaped free of the dying animal and continued to direct the surviving troops. He swung himself onto the first sound horse he could find and continued to lead the troops. Bullets were flying all around him, but he seemed unaffected. As Aaron admired Washington's bravery, determination, and leadership the scene faded, and he was again seated at the large gold table in heaven.

"More than half of our army was killed or wounded." Washington's voice was solemn and brimmed with sadness. "All of the British officers on horseback, except me, were slain or disabled. There is no doubt that I was protected by the Hand of God. 'By the all-powerful dispensations of Providence, I [was] protected beyond all human probability, or expectation; for I had four bullets through my coat, and two horses shot under me, yet escaped unhurt, though death was leveling my companions on every side of me!'[7] Our military surgeon, Dr. James Craik witnessed the events of the battle and wrote, 'I expected every moment to see [Washington] fall. His duty and situation exposed him to every danger. Nothing but the superintending care of Providence could have saved him from the fate of all around him.'[8]

"Years following the battle, I read accounts from various Indian warriors who played leading parts in this bloody battle. One related, 'Washington was never born to be killed by a bullet! For I had seventeen fair fires at him with my rifle, and after all could not bring him to the ground.'[9] And Redhawk stated, 'I fired eleven deliberate shots at that man but could not touch him. I gave over any further attempt, believing he was protected by the Great Spirit, and could not be killed.'[10]

"Years later, while working with a group of woodsmen, I was approached by a group of Indians. One of the Indians, who led the attack years earlier, said through an interpreter, 'I am a chief and ruler over many tribes. My influence extends to the waters of the great lakes, and to the far Blue Mountains. I have traveled a long and weary path, that I might see the young warrior of the great battle. It was on the day when the white man's blood mixed with the streams of our forest that I first beheld this chief. I called to my young men and said, mark yon tall and daring warrior? . . . Quick, let your aim be certain, and he dies. Our rifles were leveled, rifles which, but for him, knew not how to miss—twas all in vain, a power mightier far than we, shielded him from harm. He cannot die in battle. I am old, and soon shall be gathered to the great council-fire of my fathers, in the land of shades, but ere I go, there is a something bids me speak in the voice of prophecy. Listen! The Great Spirit protects that man, and guides his destinies—he will become the chief of nations, and a people yet unborn will hail him as the founder of a mighty empire.'[11]

"Aaron, today you should have died from gunshot wounds, but God has protected and preserved you as he preserved me years ago. Just as I was an instrument in the hands of God to win the Revolutionary War to establish the United States of America, you will be an instrument in the hands of God to restore the United States of America to the great and free land it was established to be. The assassination attempt that happened today and the miracle of your protection by Divine Providence will awaken inside of Americans across the country the desire to fight for liberties and to bring them to a remembrance that our country is a country whose motto is 'In God We Trust.'"

Washington continued, "God raises up, protects, and inspires noble men and women to bring about His purposes. It took a revolutionary war to obtain our freedom from England, and it will take a war to reclaim our country's freedom. However, it will not be a war with guns but will be a war of words, education, and the unity and vigorous effort of each American to support, defend and live the principles of freedom found in the inspired Constitution. You have been protected and preserved by God for the mission you are to complete when you return to earth. Know that God will be with you and that each of us at this table will be with you in spirit to guide, direct, and support you in your mission to restore the United States of America to the land of the free and home of the brave."

As George Washington spoke, the Spirit of God overwhelmed Aaron, and he could feel the mantle of responsibility that was on his shoulders. He was filled with gratitude for the protection he had received at the hand of the Almighty and was filled with increased courage and determination to meet the challenges ahead and lead the country to its next grand victory. Aaron declared, "I owe my life to God, and I will serve Him in every way I can.[12] What do I need to do?"

As Aaron waited for an answer, he glanced around the table. He immediately recognized Abraham Lincoln, Benjamin Franklin, Thomas Jefferson, and others.

George Washington answered, "Citizens need to know the inspired principles of the Constitution in the tradition of the Founders, so they can oppose any infringement of them. Are your citizens aware of the principles of the Constitution? Are they abiding by these principles and teaching them to others? Can they defend the Constitution? Can they recognize when a law is unconstitutional? The great Republic of America will only endure as long as the ideas of the men who founded it continue dominant."[13]

Benjamin Franklin then added, "'A nation of well-informed men who have been taught to know and prize the rights which God has given them cannot be enslaved. It is in the region of ignorance that tyranny begins.'[14] 'Education is a better safeguard of liberty than a standing army.'[15]"

Thomas Jefferson warned, "'If a nation expects to be ignorant and free, in a state of civilization, it expects what never was and never will be.'[16] Education is essential for the preservation of freedom against the aspiring tyrants who would have citizens ignorantly vote themselves into bondage."

Abraham Lincoln spoke with tears in his eyes, "It has saddened me to watch over the years as some of the greatest phrases in American history have been dropped from school textbooks while principles of socialism have crept in. You must ensure our children are taught the principles of freedom to ensure liberty continues to future generations. 'The philosophy of the school room in one generation will be the philosophy of government in the next.'[17]"

The room fell silent once more as Washington spoke. "The Lord has assembled here today many who were great instruments in His hands throughout the history of America. They will share with you stories on the divine destiny of America and teach you the principles that are the foundation of freedom and prosperity. What you learn today will help you change the course of America. Each leader at this table is here to assist you in turning America from the path of destruction."

CHAPTER 3:

DISCOVERY OF THE AMERICAS

Aaron sat in profound thought as he pondered on the wisdom shared by many of his heroes whom he had studied and sought to emulate. George Washington began to introduce one of the men at the table saying, "God preserved America from the knowledge of other nations until it was time for Him to establish a nation of liberty where people would be free to worship and create. Christopher Columbus was one of the world's greatest navigators and explorers who sought the guidance of God and recognized that his great accomplishments were the result of being an instrument in the hands of the Lord."

Columbus stood at the edge of the table and began, "It is very clear to me that my dream to sail the ocean was inspired by the Lord. I studied scripture, cosmography, history, chronicles, philosophy, and many of the other arts, and the Lord opened my understanding. I could sense his hand upon me, so that it became clear to me that it was feasible to navigate the ocean to the west. God unlocked within me the determination to execute this idea. I attest that the Spirit, with marvelous rays of light, consoled me through the holy and sacred scriptures, a strong and clear testimony, with forty-four books of the Old Testament and four Gospels with twenty-three Epistles of those blessed Apostles encouraging me to proceed, and continually, without ceasing for a moment, they inflamed me with a sense of great urgency. No one should be afraid to take on any enterprise in the name of our Savior."[18]

As Columbus began teaching with an emphasis on the Bible and the Holy Spirit, Aaron could see that it was extremely important for this brave explorer to give all the glory of his achievement to God. Aaron met Columbus's eyes with understanding as Columbus continued.

"Even though my quest was inspired by God and had his blessing, I was met with enormous challenges that had to be overcome. I searched diligently for someone to fund my ventures and was met with many rejections. 'Those who heard of my [adventurous enterprise] called it foolish, mocked me, and laughed. But who can doubt but that the Holy Ghost inspired me?'[19] After two decades of searching, Queen Isabella of Spain agreed to support my quest and the planning and preparations began.

"On the evening of August 3, 1492, I left from Spain with three ships, the *Niña*, the *Pinta*, and the *Santa Maria*. Sixty-eight days after leaving Spain, my crew began to lose hope of ever reaching our destination."

As Columbus recounted his story, Aaron heard the sounds of the ocean waves and felt the mist of salt water across his face. He looked around and found himself aboard the Santa Maria. Aaron saw a group on the other side of the ship and walked toward them to see what was happening. The crew was around Columbus and one of the men said, "The nearly continuous winds blowing from east to west will make it impossible to return home, and we have passed all projections of when land was supposed to be reached."

One of the officers turned to face Columbus and said, "It is time we turn back and return to Spain, or we are all going to die."

Columbus answered, "God has given us the winds to take us this far, and He will give us the winds to return home."

Aaron could see that the officers and crew were not going to take no for an answer as several men pulled out weapons. One crew member pointed his knife at Columbus saying, "You will turn this ship around now, or we will kill you, throw you into the sea, and turn the ship around ourselves." The crew, which now resembled an angry mob, shouted in agreement and waved their weapons. Aaron could see the fear in their eyes, and their desperation to return home.

Columbus remained calm and continued, "God gave you the faith and the courage to begin this journey. Now let God give you the faith and the courage to continue the journey.[20] Let us stay our course for two more days and see if God will grant us the victory and great success we sought of this enterprise."

Aaron watched as Columbus's words, faith, and determination softened the crew. The men began to look at each other, and with slight nods, all seemed to be in agreement to persist for two more days. Without saying a word, they began to part and return to their duties on the ship.

Columbus walked silently to the other end of the ship. Aaron followed him, knowing that he could not be seen or heard. He entered with Columbus into his private quarters and watched as he removed his hat and placed it upon the small desk. Columbus then went to his knees and began to pray. Aaron watched as he knelt in silence for what seemed like an eternity. The strength, peace, and love of the Savior and His Holy Spirit filled the room. Aaron could feel the divine importance of this moment in history.

After several minutes, Columbus rose from his knees and took a seat at his desk. He opened a book and began to write. As he was writing, Aaron walked up behind the chair and looked over Columbus's shoulder to see the words flow from his pen. Aaron read each word as Columbus wrote, "The men lost all patience and faith. I encouraged them in the best manner I could, and then I 'prayed mightily to the Lord'[21] and I felt that having come so far, we must continue on till with the help of the Lord, we should arrive."[22]

As Columbus continued to write, Aaron could no longer make out the words, and the scene faded from his view. He looked up and found himself back at the large gold table in heaven as Columbus continued to tell the story. "The next day we spotted land birds and other signs of nearing land and at 2 a.m. 'on October 12, with the Pinta sailing ahead, the weather cleared. In the moonlight one of the sailors on the Pinta, Juan Rodriquez Bermejo, saw a white sand beach and land beyond it. After his shout of 'Land! Land!' the Pinta's crew raised a flag on its highest mast and fired a cannon.'[23] I organized a landing party which rowed to the white sandy beaches. I disembarked the boat and fell to my knees and offered a prayer of thanks and named the island San Salvador (Holy Savior), for it was by His guidance and protection that the discovery was made.[24]

"I had achieved my inspired dream of sailing the Atlantic, the world was changed forever, and the purposes of God were moved forward. This was the early beginnings of God's plan to create a free nation. The great success of this enterprise is not to be ascribed to my own merits, but to the Lord often granting to men what they never imagine themselves capable of effecting, as He is accustomed to hearing the prayers of His servants even in that which appears impossible.[25] Aaron, as an instrument in the hands of God, you will achieve many things which those around you will say are impossible."

Columbus looked Aaron directly in the eyes and said, "Never be afraid to take on a challenge in the name of the Lord."

CHAPTER 4:
THE ENVELOPES

Paula Brackett sat at her desk in the Eisenhower Executive Office Building in Washington, DC with her planner opened and a pen in hand. Many requests came in every day for Vice President Banner's time. One of Paula's more difficult jobs as his Chief of Staff was to keep everything organized and running smoothly.

It had been an extremely busy morning, but Paula was used to having more tasks to complete than there were hours in a day. She went through her to-do list and checked off the many items she had completed that morning and then looked to see which task she should work on next.

"Paula! Paula! Are you watching the news? Did you hear?" Phil Meriman poked his head in Paula's office, his voice urgent. "Aaron Banner has been shot and was rushed to the hospital."

Paula leaped from her chair in terrifying alarm. She had a television in her office, but it was rarely on so she could focus on her work. She dashed across the room and grabbed the remote to turn on the news. She didn't have to search for the story. Every channel was focused on the news of the shooting. Paula could hear Phil down the hall, repeating the devastating news.

The face of Mary Banner filled the TV screen as reporters rushed to catch the moment she arrived at the hospital to be with her husband. Paula saw the shocked and scared look on her face. The reporters were asking many questions, but Mary's security detail cleared the way for her, and she was swept through the hospital doors, leaving the reporters with speculation and sparse facts to repeat.

Paula sat back at her desk with her hands clinched together, holding them to her mouth. Tears filled her eyes as she said a prayer for Aaron, his family, and those at Stanford Hospital caring for him. As she prayed, she remembered an unusual encounter with Aaron the previous week. He had given her a sealed envelope and told her to keep it safe.

"I trust you'll never have to open this," Aaron had reassured Paula as he pressed the envelope into her hand, "But just in case, I think you should have this. Open it only if something happens to me." When Paula pressed him on the matter, he only told her not to worry and not to speak of it further, and to keep the envelope secret and safe until he reclaimed it himself or something happened to him. Paula tucked the envelope in a file and marked it as some inconsequential paperwork that no one would have reason to look at, and had not thought much about it since. It was a brief encounter that neither of them discussed in the days that followed.

Paula pulled out the file and took out the plain white envelope with shaking hands. She tore open the seal and found a handwritten note inside and began to read with equal parts of curiosity and dread.

Paula,

I was hoping not to involve you in this, but if you are reading this letter, my worst fears have been realized. I now call upon you to carry out your patriotic duty to this great nation. I have recently received information pointing to bribery, corruption, and other high crimes by several congressmen, senators, and perhaps even the President himself. In order to increase their power, control, and wealth, they have organized themselves within our government to undermine our Constitution and establish a socialistic society and government. These are crimes of a most heinous nature, so I hesitate to make them known without solid proof. I have collected some evidence and have hidden it in five separate envelopes, which I need you to retrieve for me. They are all in locations you routinely visit as you carry out your duties as Chief of Staff, so you should be able to get to them without arousing any suspicion. Be warned, though, that there are many who would rather see you harmed than have this evidence brought to light. There are only a few whom I trust, and I ask you to deliver these envelopes to them. I have listed their names and the locations of the envelopes on the back of this letter. You have both courage and dedication, and I know you love this country as I do. I call on you to put all of your resources and bravery to this task. May God be with you.

Your servant,

Aaron Banner

Paula drew in a deep breath. She had often been called efficient and friendly, but no one had called her courageous. She was frightened at the enormous responsibility and terrified at the thought that people might try to harm or even kill her to keep her from it. But Aaron was right, she did love her country, and his trust in her buoyed her courage. Paula scanned the names Aaron had written on the back of his letter. Some she knew personally, some she recognized, but others she did not know at all.

> *Eric Fisher, Associate Attorney General*
> *Stanley Johnson, FBI Special Agent*
> *Charles Morell, Deputy Director of the National*
> *   Clandestine Service*
> *Josh Wilson, CIA Agent*
> *Jacob Pryor, Senator*

The locations of the envelopes and combinations were there as well. Paula took a deep breath and read.

1. Top of our post office box.
2. Compartments in wood chest in the Vice President's Ceremonial Office: there are six wood pegs on the front of the chest that when turned to the appropriate positions open a secret compartment. There is a subtle line on each of the pegs that is to be turned to the correct position to unlock the secret compartment. The position of the line coincides with the positions of the numbers on a clock

with twelve being straight up. Beginning with the peg on the left, the combination is 12, 5, 7, 11, 3, 9. When the pegs are in the correct positions the secret compartment will reveal itself.

3. Tunnel between Eisenhower Executive Building and White House: this envelope is hidden under the carpet. Find the fifth light fixture from the Eisenhower Executive Building toward the White House. On the right side of the wall in alignment with the fifth light fixture, pull the carpet back from the tacks, and you will see the envelope. This is a point in the tunnel where you cannot be seen from a distance in either direction and is not picked up by the security cameras, so you will be able to pull back the carpet without being noticed.

4. Wall safe behind George Washington picture in my office: combination 5, 9, 1, 5, 4, 2.

5. Bottom drawer of the large file cabinet in my office: envelope is mixed in with paper in file labeled "Mailing Lists."

As she scanned through the list, she put together a plan of action in her mind. The first envelope to secure would be the one in the Vice President's Ceremonial Office. It was not far from where she was and no one would question her being there.

"That one should be easy enough," Paula reasoned. She folded the letter up and stuffed it into the zippered pocket inside her bag. She took the pen and small notebook she always carried with her to scribble down her thoughts. She crossed the room to the television, which was still relating the same few details they had about the shooting. She turned off the TV and closed her eyes.

She knew that Aaron and everyone in America needed her help, and she knew she needed the guidance, support, and miracles of God to be with her if she was to fulfill the task before her.

"Please, Lord," she began to pray. "Bless me with the courage and strength to secure and deliver these important envelopes. Please prepare my path and guide me. Please protect me from harm. Please frustrate the efforts of those fighting against us and obscure my efforts from their view. And please, Lord, bless Aaron Banner and his family."

Paula took another deep breath and left her office.

CHAPTER 5:
REVOLUTIONARY PATRIOTS

Columbus looked to President Washington and took his seat. Washington turned to face Columbus and said, "Christopher, we are all grateful for the inspired role you played in the establishment of a free nation. Thank you for sharing your story and inspiration with Aaron."

Aaron and the other men who gathered at the table added words of gratitude, and Columbus nodded his head in humble acknowledgement.

Washington turned back to Aaron. "Are you ready to meet the next person to address you?" Aaron was anxious to see what would transpire next. A man at the table rose to his feet, but Aaron did not recognize him, so he looked to Washington for an introduction.

Washington did not immediately share the identity of this man, but instead began a tale from United States history. "Aaron, in the years prior to the establishment of the United States of America, there were many brave men and women who sacrificed much to achieve the inspired dream of a free nation. On July 2, 1776, I wrote to my troops saying, 'The fate of unborn millions will now depend, under God, on the courage and conduct of this army. . . Let us therefore rely upon the goodness of the cause, and the aid of the Supreme Being, in whose hands victory is.'[26] Two hundred thousand brave soldiers fought during the Revolutionary War knowing they would experience pain, sorrow, loss, and possible death. These patriots were willing to make these sacrifices, though, for the benefit of their children and their children's children. Unfortunately, few of the events of these exalted patriots have been preserved. Among those who, in the crisis that tried men's souls, devoted their best years to the service of their country was Benjamin Birdsall. One example of Captain Birdsall's devotion occurred when the British captured an American vessel filled with flour for our army. Captain Birdsall believed he could retake the ship and volunteered to lead the fight personally. His request was granted, and with a few carefully chosen men, they set out and succeeded in recapturing the ship from the British. However, during the mission, Captain Birdsall and one of his men were taken prisoner by the enemy.[27] I will let Captain Birdsall tell you the rest of the story."

Captain Birdsall began, "The British controlled New York for nearly the entire period of the Revolutionary War, and it was made their headquarters for the foulest tyranny over helpless prisoners. The conditions were deplorable and the British were often heartless. I was one of many taken prisoner, and I know firsthand of the suffering that was experienced. It began as soon as I was brought to the Provost Marshal, William Cunningham."

There was terrible grief in Birdsall's voice, a heavy quality that could only have been brought about through exquisite suffering. Aaron waited for the moment when the horrors being described would come to life before his eyes, but Captain Birdsall spoke on, and no prison appeared. Aaron could see the profound emotion in Birdsall's eyes and realized that hearing the story firsthand from a man who experienced this would provide a clear picture of the experience of those taken as prisoners of war.

"I was formally introduced to Cunningham, and my name, age, and rank were recorded. As you might imagine, the welfare of my family was foremost in my mind. I knew that they would be frantic with worry, and I sought to alleviate their fears. I asked Cunningham for a pen and paper. Cunningham drew his sword and stabbed me through the shoulder,[28] yelling, 'damned rebel.'[29] In pain and bleeding freely, I was dragged to a gloomy, overcrowded cell, with no thought of treating my wound. I did my best to stop the bleeding and bandage my shoulder. The conditions in the prison at times seemed almost too much to bear, and the thought of dying was a relief. It was the love of my family, my belief in the glorious cause of America, and my faith in God that gave me the strength to carry on.

"My cell was so crowded that as we tried to sleep on the hard plank floor, we could only change positions by all turning over at once, at the words, right or left. When we had food given to us, it was of poorest quality. At times, there was no food at all, and thousands of my fellow prisoners died of starvation. Watching those determined patriots waste away, becoming weaker and weaker until they finally could hold on no longer was..."

Birdsall paused and Aaron found himself riveted to Captain

Birdsall's eyes. He could see all of the sorrow and pain that Birdsall felt as he relived the experience.

Birdsall continued, "When gifts were sent to me or any of the others in the prison, Cunningham would devour or destroy such offerings of affection in our presence to gratify his cruel propensities. Prior to our service in the war, many of us were gentlemen of fortune and education who had lived in the enjoyment of the luxuries and refined pleasures of elegant social life. Now we were subjected to the worst living conditions and abuse imaginable.

"Many of these brave men were packed by the thousands into the hulls of prison ships which were filled with vermin, putrid air, stifling heat, the sighs of the acutely distressed, and the groans of the dying. Each morning, the hatch was opened with the harsh order, 'Rebels, turn out your dead.' The dead were selected from the living and conveyed under guard in a boat to the shore by their companions, who hastily buried them. So shallow were the graves that while they were burying the newly dead, the action of the waves and the drifting of the loose sand often exposed the bones of those previously buried. Year after year, this revolting practice continued.[30] I was one of the few prisoners who survived. Over seventeen thousand of the twenty-five thousand revolutionary prisoners of war made the ultimate sacrifice and gave their life in the fight for independence.[31]"

Birdsall's voice quivered as he spoke, and the room was permeated by the emotion of his story. Aaron had read stories of the revolutionary prisoners of war, but hearing it firsthand penetrated his soul and gratitude filled his heart for the sacrifice these men had made for the freedoms he enjoyed.

Birdsall continued, "One of the most outrageous of all the crimes committed by Cunningham was the hanging of 275 of these American prisoners of war without trial and in utter repudiation of all existing articles of war. All of these patriots could have betrayed the cause of liberty and independence in exchange for their lives but chose death over such a betrayal. All they had to do was to sign a document of allegiance to the Crown and receive a free pardon by enlisting in the British army or navy. Not one would sign such a document.[32] All stayed true to the ideals of a free and independent nation.

"So many great men died." Captain Birdsall lowered his head and closed his eyes for a moment. Aaron could only imagine the horrors he experienced as hundreds of Americans died around him. The Captain reached into his pocket and pulled out a piece of paper. His voice shook off his sorrow and elevated to a tone of honor and pride. "In the dark hours of 1780, when nearly all hope of independence had fled forever, and when the deserter and traitor stalked over the land in fearful combination, the imprisoned and dying patriots reached forth their skeleton hands and bequeathed a task to their countrymen in their dying hours."

Captain Birdsall looked at the paper he had pulled from his pocket and began to read, "'If you are victorious, and our country emerges free and independent from the contest in which she is now engaged, but the end of which we are not permitted to see, bury us in her soil, and engrave our names on the monument you shall erect over our bones, as victims who willingly surrendered their lives as a portion of the price paid for your liberties, and our departed spirits will never murmur, or regret the sacrifice we made to obtain for you the blessings you enjoy.'[33]"

Captain Birdsall folded up the piece of paper and returned it to his pocket and said, "'If there is any class of patriots more deserving of the gratitude of a nation than another, it is these captives, who dwelt in the dungeons for their country's sake.'[34]"

Captain Birdsall looked directly into Aaron's eyes and brought his hand up and down as he continued, "Aaron, you must lead a new group of patriots to restore the freedom we fought and sacrificed so much for. Today the country must decide to choose liberty and independence or bondage and misery. Some Americans are betraying the cause of liberty and independence by seeking and accepting government handouts and assistance. Some Americans are willing to sell their freedom for government-provided retirement or health care. Americans must resist and fight against the idea that the government should provide the necessities of life. As responsibility is shifted from the people to the government, freedom is eroded. Today America is facing economic challenges, and it is during times of trial and crisis that many will sell their freedom for the illusion of government security. In response to these challenges, larger government is not the solution. Any society that gives up liberty in hopes of security will find they lose both. Freedom and security are only to be found in liberty, industry, and production.

"America needs modern patriots to resist and fight against the unconstitutional and tyrannical efforts of the American government. The God of heaven sent some of the wisest, noblest, and bravest men and women to lay the foundation of a free America, and God has again sent many wise, noble, and brave men and women to preserve it. The blessed beneficiaries, of the suffering and sacrifices made by your revolutionary ancestors, face difficult days in America. Action must be taken to once again establish a government that follows the inspired Constitution. May God bless you to lead a group of modern patriots full of the faith, courage, and determination needed to preserve and restore freedom. May you honor by your actions and always remember the revolutionary patriots who pledged their lives, their fortunes, and their sacred honor to secure your freedom."

Captain Birdsall took his seat and Aaron could feel the weight of his charge settle upon him. With tears running down his face, Aaron asked President Washington if he could offer a word of prayer. Washington nodded in the affirmative. Aaron bowed his head and offered a prayer aloud. "Our Father who art in heaven, hollowed be Thy name. I wish to express gratitude for the many men and women who have served and sacrificed to secure our country's freedom. I feel unequal to such a task. Please strengthen and guide me as we seek to restore and preserve the United States of America. Amen."

CHAPTER 6:
CONSTITUTIONAL CONVENTION

President Washington thanked Aaron for his prayer and then assured him saying, "I know how you feel, Aaron. On June 15, 1775, the Continental Congress met to elect a general for the Continental Army for the defense of American liberty. Each member of Congress cast their vote by ballot, and I was unanimously chosen to be the supreme commander of the forces to secure an independent and free nation. I felt great distress that my abilities and military experience may not be equal to such an extensive and important trust. However, as the Congress desired it, I entered upon the momentous duty, and exerted every power I possessed in their service and for support of the glorious cause.[35] I assure you, just as I did not play my part alone, the Lord will be with you. 'Liberty, honor and safety are all at stake; and I trust Providence will smile upon our efforts, and establish us once more, the inhabitants of a free and happy country.'[36]

"Aaron, you must restore the Constitution of our great country. I know you are a scholar of the Constitution, but I think you will still enjoy hearing directly from the men who took part in the creation of this inspired document which is to be the 'Supreme Law of the land.'[37] We will start with the Father of the Constitution, James Madison. James 'has the distinction of being the shortest President in US history . . . but his intellect [is] inversely proportional to his physical stature.'[38] James 'nobly fulfilled his destinies as a man and a Christian. He . . . improved his own condition by improving that of his country. [He was one of the] patriots and heroes under whose guidance the revolution of American Independence was begun and continued and completed.'[39]"

James Madison rose to his feet, but his head did not rise much above the other men's heads who were seated. "I will not be the only one to discuss the Constitution with you today," Madison told Aaron by way of greeting. "I am honored to tell you about the Constitutional Convention of 1787. Following victory in the Revolutionary War, the American colonies had the unique opportunity of establishing a new country and government. The Articles of Confederation were the first governing document that loosely tied the newly independent thirteen colonies, but they were incomplete and inadequate to completely govern the new nation. To establish a constitution and a new form of government, the Constitutional Convention was organized and held in Philadelphia."

As Madison spoke, the gold table and room slowly faded around him as a new scene took its place. As Aaron looked around, he recognized that he was in the assembly room of Independence Hall. He had visited Independence Hall on numerous occasions and considered the historic building to be sacred ground since it had been the host of numerous scenes of great courage and wisdom.

Aaron gazed around the room and saw fifty-five men seated in the forty-foot square room. George Washington, presiding over the convention, sat at a raised table. The raised table sat in the center of the east wall with a fireplace on each side. The other fifty-four delegates sat at tables throughout the room facing Washington. One of the men stood to address those present. Aaron immediately recognized the man to be Benjamin Franklin. Confident and self-assured, he motioned for the meeting to begin with a prayer.

Franklin stated with utter sincerity, "'God governs in the affairs of men. And if a sparrow cannot fall to the ground without His notice, is it probable that an empire can rise without his aid? We have been assured, sir, in the sacred writings that except the Lord build the house, they labor in vain that build it. I firmly believe this, and I also believe without his concurring aid we shall succeed in this political building no better than the builders of Babel.'[40]"

Franklin's voice was raised by the end of his speech. Aaron enjoyed reading his speeches, but actually hearing Benjamin Franklin in person exceeded his highest expectations. Aaron watched as the motion for prayer was unanimously accepted by the fifty-five leaders assembled. Aaron turned to his right to find that the James Madison from heaven was sitting by his side.

The scene before him froze as Madison spoke. "We worked over the next four months under the guidance and inspiration of the Almighty to draft the Constitution of the United States of America. This document was the foundation of the newly formed republic. In

September of 1787, the written Constitution was complete and ready to be signed; however, many of the fifty-five delegates were hesitant to sign the document. You have seen the beginning of the convention. Now you will see the conclusion."

Aaron watched as sound and movement returned to the assembly room. He feasted upon the scene as Benjamin Franklin once more rose to his feet and spoke. "'I confess that I do not entirely approve of this Constitution at present . . . For when you assemble a number of men to have the advantage of their joint wisdom, you inevitably assemble with those men all their prejudices, their passions, their errors of opinion, their local interests, and their selfish views. From such an assembly can a perfect production be expected? It therefore astonishes me, sir, to find this system approaching so near to perfection as it does; and I think it will astonish our enemies. . . I hope therefore that for our own sakes, as a part of the people, and for the sake of our posterity, we shall act heartily and unanimously in recommending this Constitution.'⁴¹"

Aaron was greatly impressed at the persuasive powers Franklin used to urge all delegates to sign the Constitution. Following the speech, he watched as the delegates assembled around the Constitution and began to sign.

He walked toward the group to get a closer view, and as he neared Franklin, he heard him speaking to a few of the people around him.

"Often during the past four months of this convention, I looked at the sun on the chair of General Washington."

Aaron looked to the chair Washington had been sitting in. It was a wooden chair with a padded seat and arm rests. It was not much different than many of the chairs you might find at a nice dining table.

On the chair's back was the image of the top half of a sun.

Franklin continued, "From the depiction on the chair, it was hard to distinguish if it was a rising or setting sun. As I listened to the discussions and debates during our sessions, I was unable to tell whether the sun was rising or setting on our efforts. As I watch the last of the delegates sign the new Constitution, I can happily say without a doubt that it is indeed a rising and not a setting sun.[42]"

The scene faded as Aaron watched the final delegates sign this sacred document. He found himself back at the gold table in heaven and looked toward James Madison as he was the only person standing. Their eyes met as Madison began, "It was an honor to work with fifty-four other great leaders and to be a part of one of the most significant events in the history of the world. 'There never was an assembly of men, charged with a great and arduous trust, who were more pure in their motives, or more exclusively or anxiously devoted to the object committed to them, than were the members of the Convention of 1787, to the devising and proposing a constitutional system . . . [to] secure the permanent liberty and happiness of their country.'[43] 'It is impossible for the man of pious reflection not to perceive in it a finger of that Almighty hand.'[44]

"My feelings regarding the convention were shared by many. Alexander Hamilton said, 'I sincerely esteem it a system, which without the finger of God, never could have been suggested and agreed upon by such a diversity of interest.'[45] And Charles Pinckney declared, 'When the great work was done and published, I was . . . struck with amazement. Nothing less than the superintending Hand of Providence, that so miraculously carried us through the war . . .

could have brought it about so complete.'[46]

"Without a doubt, the Constitution of the United States is founded upon the Almighty's just and holy principles. His hand did guide us in its creation."

CHAPTER 7:
SECURING THE ENVELOPES

Paula tried to act naturally as she walked down the hall of the Eisenhower Executive Office Building, where both her office and the Vice President's Ceremonial Office were located. She couldn't help but feel every eye was on her. She pulled open the door to the Ceremonial Office and was relieved to find the room vacant.

"Relax," she told herself as she entered this historic and beautiful room. A large conference table surrounded by fourteen chairs sat in the middle, with the Vice President's desk on one end and couches on the other. The wood floor was a combination of mahogany, white maple, and cherry. The two fireplaces were original Belgian black marble. Three large chandeliers hung from the eighteen-foot ceiling. The perimeter of the room was filled with decorative tables, cabinets, and display cases.

Paula glanced over each shoulder to ensure no one had followed her and then closed the door. The wooden chest Aaron Banner had specified in the letter was easy to spot. It sat on one of the tables near the back of the room. She admired its construction as she reached to touch the smooth wooden pegs that made up a kind of combination lock. Paula pulled out the letter that Aaron had left for her, wanting to be sure she turned the knobs to the correct position.

"First knob, twelve noon," she read aloud, turning the knob as she spoke. She heard an almost inaudible click come from the box. "Second knob, five o'clock." She paused for a moment and took a deep breath to try and calm herself.

She turned the third and fourth knobs to their proper positions. As she turned the fifth knob, she heard the door open behind her. Her heart rate surged, causing her body to sweat. As she turned to the door, she heard the words, "What are you doing in here?" It was a member of the building security team, more intimidating in his uniform than she had ever noticed before.

Paula answered in a remarkably calm voice. "With all that has happened, I came in here for a few moments of solitude." She saw his body visibly relax as he recognized her.

"Sorry for the intrusion, Mrs. Brackett. Normally, I would not have even asked, but we're all on a heightened level of security right now."

"That's all right," Paula told him, "I appreciate your watching over our office." She was sincere in her gratitude, and the security agent seemed to feel it and said, "I hope the Vice President recovers soon, Ma'am."

Paula thanked him as he turned to go, and he nodded as he closed the door behind him. She took a deep breath and turned back to the chest.

"Fifth knob, three o'clock," she whispered, turning the smooth wooden peg. Only one more and she would have it. As the sixth knob slid into place, the box made a louder clicking noise, and a panel at the bottom of the box sprang open about an inch. Paula pulled the drawer open to see a single white envelope resting inside. She picked it up and noted the weight. There seemed to be something small and rectangular in the corner of the envelope.

"A jump drive," she guessed as she put the envelope into her purse and zipped it closed.

"One down, four to go," she thought to herself as she left the office. She walked down the hallway toward the elevators. The tunnel to the West Wing of the White House was well lit and very secure, but Paula was apprehensive heading down to it now.

Because of the heightened security, she had to show her badge several times before she actually made it into the tunnel. She told herself that meant anyone after her would have to show proper clearance as well. However, if Vice President Banner had evidence against powerful politicians, they would have many staff members with that clearance. Her footsteps quickened.

As she walked down the tunnel, she counted the light fixtures to make a mental note of the fifth one, so she could quickly stop and secure the envelope under the carpet on her return to the Eisenhower Building. Paula had made this walk through the tunnel hundreds of times, but today it seemed longer and darker than normal. As she came to the exit of the tunnel, Paula was again met by security, and her ID and security clearance were checked.

On her way to the Vice President's office, she was stopped several times by those wishing her well and those who asked if she had any new information on Aaron's condition. As she was a frequent visitor to the West Wing, no one considered it out of the ordinary that she would be there now. As Paula stepped into the hall where Vice President Banner's office was located, she looked around, checking to see if the hallway was clear, then slipped into the office, closing the door firmly behind her.

Looking around the room, Paula immediately felt that something was amiss. The angle of the computer monitor was strange, the placement of items on the desk was different, and Aaron's chair was not tucked neatly under the desk like he usually left it. Although the changes were small, it seemed that someone had been in the office searching for something.

She anxiously surveyed the room as she walked backwards toward the portrait of George Washington hanging on the wall. Pushing the painting aside, she found the wall safe just as Aaron had told her in the letter. She entered the code, looking nervously over her shoulder as she did so. The door swung open easily, but Paula's heart sank as she saw that it was completely empty.

This confirmed in her mind that people inside the White House were involved in the shooting of Vice President Banner and were seeking to destroy any incriminating evidence he had obtained. If they had been willing to assassinate the Vice President, Paula had no doubt she would be killed if they knew what she was doing.

The safe was an obvious place to keep something of importance, but hopefully the intruder and thief had not found the information hidden in the file. "Let's see if they found you," Paula said to herself as she opened the filing cabinet drawer.

"Please, please, please," Paula whispered to herself, hurriedly flipping through the files. The one labeled "mailing list" was a full one, and Paula pulled it from the drawer to thumb through it. She found an envelope that looked just like the last one she had found, with the same sort of object sealed within. She put the envelope in a different pocket of her purse than the first, returned the file, and closed the drawer. Paula now had two of the five envelopes.

However, the missing envelope greatly troubled her and heightened her concern that she could be in danger. She had only been in Aaron's office for a few minutes but was anxious to exit the White House as quickly as possible as she wondered who might be watching her. The White House felt more like a den of robbers and thieves than the headquarters of the United States.

Paula made her way quickly back to the tunnel, only stopping to show her badge at the appropriate checkpoints. The depths of the tunnel felt even more ominous to her as she descended the stairs and hurried through it as quickly as she could without breaking into a run.

As Paula approached the designated light fixture, she began walking near the wall. Before bending down to more closely examine the carpeting, a cool breeze brushed past, stirring her hair. She turned around and saw no one, but had the sudden, overwhelming feeling that someone was watching her. She waited silently for a moment, watching for anyone else in the tunnel, but no one approached her from either direction.

She bent down, deciding that her imagination was getting the best of her. Laying her purse on the carpet, she quickly ran her hand along the edge where the carpet met the wall, feeling for a loose patch. She found the spot where the adhesion to the floor had been loosened and pulled back the carpet to find the hidden envelope.

She quickly stood up and secured the envelope in her purse as she walked along the wall to the exit of the tunnel and entered the Eisenhower Building. She desperately wished she could confide in her coworkers, but she knew that secrecy was key to her success. The more people who knew what she was doing, the more danger she would be in.

Paula exited the building and walked to her car to drive to the post office, secure the last envelope, and begin the deliveries. She was only a few feet from her vehicle when she came to a sudden stop. She had seen too many action movies where someone was blown up by a car bomb and did not want to suffer a similar fate.

She looked at her car, wondering if it seemed different since she parked it that morning. She pulled her keys from her bag and held the remote starter in her hand. She backed away about thirty feet then pressed the remote start button with her eyes closed. The engine started without incident, so she pushed the unlock button and the doors released with a beep. She opened the door and slid into her seat, relieved there was no explosion and happy to still be alive and breathing.

"Too many episodes of *24*," she said aloud, as she shifted into reverse and backed out of her spot. The radio was tuned to her favorite station, which helped to calm her a bit. She pulled from the parking lot and headed to the post office, located just a few minutes away. As Paula entered through the automatic doors of the building, she found the post office nearly empty. She tried to look natural as she strode to the box with key in hand. She glanced about to see if anyone seemed too interested in her actions. There were a few other people collecting mail from their boxes, but nothing seemed to be out of the ordinary.

She opened the box to see several letters at the bottom. She reached in and felt for the envelope that was to be taped to the top of the box. Her fingers found it easily. She unpeeled the tape and joined the envelope with the letters at the bottom of the box. She then pulled the envelopes from the box, placed them in her bag, and headed to her car.

Once in her car, she took a moment to think. She had retrieved all of the envelopes except the one that had been stolen from the Vice President's wall safe. She pulled out her notebook and pen from her bag, ready to plan her deliveries. She went over the list of recipients, tapping her pen against the notebook as she mapped out her course.

She decided she would first make the ten mile drive to Langley where both CIA Agent Josh Wilson and Deputy Director of the National Clandestine Service, Charles Morell, had their offices. She could then go to the FBI building, the Department of Justice Building, and finally the Senate Office Building, all of which were within two miles of the White House. With her plan set, she started her car and headed for the Keys Bridge. She felt a sense of relief as she thought, "Within the hour, all of the envelopes should be delivered and my task complete."

CHAPTER 8:

PILLAR 1—DIVINELY GRANTED RIGHTS

James Madison sat down and Washington smiled at Aaron's expression as he sat in profound thought and awe. "I can see you enjoyed your visit to the assembly hall," Washington commented with a slight grin.

Aaron answered, "The Spirit of God and the love of liberty that permeated the room is an experience I will never forget. I have read the accounts of the Constitutional Convention, but experiencing it in person was illuminating."

"I am confident your illumination will continue as you are taught by your next instructor," Washington said. "Even among the exceptional group of Founding Fathers, Thomas Jefferson was a giant."

James Madison, who was just five feet four inches tall and weighed one hundred pounds, joked, "Next, to me, anyone is a giant."

A few around the table chuckled, and Washington continued, "Thomas authored the Declaration of Independence and the Statute of

Virginia for Religious Freedom. He served as the third President of the United States and founded the University of Virginia. He faithfully served his country for over five decades."

Thomas Jefferson, one of the tallest founding fathers at six feet two inches, with long slender limbs, rose to his feet and began to speak. "Do you realize the great role you will play in our nation's history?"

"I'm the Vice President of the United States, and I work diligently for liberty and freedom, but I certainly wouldn't have my name mentioned with any of those at this table." Aaron replied.

"You are stronger and play a more imperative role than you realize," Jefferson said seriously. "Today is a historic day in the fight for liberty and in the fight against tyranny. In my life, I worked diligently to create, support, and defend the Constitution of the United States, and I am honored to continue to defend it today by teaching you, Aaron. Through your diligent effort in completing your divinely appointed mission, your name will be mentioned in history with the great patriots gathered here today."

Aaron nodded his head as if to say he would do all he could to save American liberty. Jefferson nodded back at Aaron and continued, "I have been asked to teach you the first of four pillars of the inspired Constitution: Divinely Granted Rights. 'I have sworn upon the altar of God eternal hostility against every form of tyranny over the mind of man. [For] the God who gave us life, gave us liberty at the same time.'[47] Our divinely granted rights can be found in the Declaration of Independence and in the Bill of Rights. 'We hold these truths to be self-evident, that all men are created equal, that they are endowed by their Creator with certain unalienable rights, that among these are life, liberty and the pursuit of happiness.'[48]"

Aaron nodded in agreement. Jefferson continued, "Many today misuse the word 'right' to claim that every American has a right to a job, food, clothes, recreation, medical care, a house, retirement, and education. 'The right to life means that a man has the right to support his life by his own work; it does not mean that others must provide him with the necessities of life. The right to property means that a man has the right to take the economic action necessary to earn property . . . it does not mean that others must provide him with property. . . There is no such thing as 'a right to a job' . . . there is only . . . a man's right to take a job if another man chooses to hire him. There is no 'right to a home' only . . . the right to build a home or to buy it.'[49]

"The proper role of government is to protect the right to pursue property, not to grant property. Government welfare programs that give citizens food, health care, or other items create a class of people who can get 'wealth without work,' which is one of the social sins that will destroy a society.[50] With government welfare, independence and work are replaced with dependence and handouts."

Aaron had seen ample evidence of this statement and said, "It is sad to watch as government welfare programs cripple the very people they claim to be helping."

"You understand the problem precisely," Jefferson said sadly. "It reminds me of a story which illustrates the dangers of dependence. In the city of St. Augustine, great flocks of seagulls starved amid plenty. Fishing was still good, but the gulls didn't know how to fish. For generations they depended on the shrimp fleet to toss them scraps from the nets. But then the fleet moved. The shrimpers had created a Welfare State for the seagulls. The big birds never bothered to learn how to fish for themselves, and they never taught their children to fish. Instead they led their little ones to the shrimp nets. Now the seagulls, the fine free birds that almost symbolize liberty itself, are starving to death because they gave in to the 'something for nothing' lure! They sacrificed their independence for a hand-out. A lot of people are like that, too. They see nothing wrong in picking delectable scraps from the tax nets of the US Government's 'shrimp fleet.' We must preserve our talents of self-sufficiency, our genius for creating things for ourselves, our sense of thrift and our true love of independence.[51] Every handout has a price and that price is a loss of freedom.

"Our rights bring with them obligations and responsibilities, not handouts and entitlements. Liberty gives us the power to think, choose, and act for ourselves. Liberty creates opportunities for growth, creation, and joy. However, liberty also creates failure, pain, and suffering. Many have tried to eliminate the failure, pain, and suffering accompanied by liberty, thinking, 'Wouldn't life be better if there was no adversity, pain, or opposition?'

"Let me now share with you what I call the parable of the two schools. In School One, you are required to study and work. Your grade is based on performance, so some will get A's and others will fail. Only those who fulfill the requirements will earn a degree. It is challenging and at times painful. In School Two, you must take tests but all the tests are multiple choice and 'C' is always the correct answer. You are required to answer 'C' for each question, and everyone who takes the test receives a perfect score. Everyone receives a degree and graduates with a perfect 4.0 GPA. It is easy. It is free from work, pain, and struggle.

Aaron, given these two scenarios, which of the two schools would you want your doctor to have attended?"

Aaron answered, "Obviously I would want a doctor from School One—especially if I wanted to live."

Jefferson smiled and said, "Of course. I share this simple example because many try to take away choice to ensure everyone succeeds, and in doing so, make it so no one succeeds. If such a medical school existed, everyone would graduate with a perfect score and a medical degree. Graduates would be given the title of doctor, but the real purpose of learning the necessary skills of surgery would not have been achieved, and thus the diploma from such an institution would be worthless. Work, pain, struggle, and failure are part of the necessary education process to produce an individual with the skills of a surgeon. If this school attempted to make everyone a surgeon, no one would become a surgeon.

"Likewise, if a government tries to make it so everyone has prosperity, it will result in no one having prosperity. When liberty, work, pain, and suffering are taken out of school, the purpose of school is defeated. If we 'try to exclude the possibility of suffering which the order of nature and the existence of free-wills involve, you find that you have excluded life itself.'[52] Liberty gives us the power to progress and improve our lives and the lives of those around us. Take away liberty and you take away progression toward greatness."

Aaron could feel Jefferson's earnestness. He was passionate about his subject. It was clear that he strongly believed that God wanted his children to be free.

"Everything we did," Jefferson continued, "was for the purpose of protecting the God-given rights we are born with. This is why we formed a democratic republic and not a pure democracy. Under the constitutional democratic republic we formed, there are God-given rights to be protected by the government, which cannot be violated or taken away, even by majority vote. The government is the protector, not the grantor, of our rights."

Aaron declared, "Sadly there are many trying to remove God from government through the fabricated disguise of 'separation of church and state.' Over the past decades, the phrase 'separation of church and state' has been used so often by courts and other organizations that many believe it to be a part of the First Amendment of the Constitution. They use you as the originator of the idea to give credibility and precedence to their claims."

Jefferson, visibly angry, hit his fist on the table and said firmly, "The phrase 'separation of church and state' is not a part of the Constitution or any other founding document. In fact, in the months of debate and discussion with eighty-nine Founding Fathers and myself in the drafting of the first amendment, the phrase was never mentioned.[53] The First Amendment was never intended to remove God from our government. The First Amendment says, 'Congress shall make no law respecting an establishment of religion or prohibiting the free exercise thereof. . .'[54]

"The First Amendment is a constitutional prohibition of a government-sponsored religion. Our purpose was to prevent the formation of a single denomination created and operated by the government as had occurred in Great Britain with the Church of England. The First Amendment simply prohibits the US government from creating and operating a church or interfering with the religious practices of its citizens. Excluding God is undoubtedly counter to the intentions of the First Amendment and the Founding Fathers. God is the foundation upon which the American republic was built. Our currency bears the inscription of the motto, 'In God We Trust,' and citizens pledge allegiance to a 'nation under God.' These phrases 'help us to keep constantly in our minds and hearts the spiritual and moral principles which alone give dignity to man, and upon which our way of life is founded.'[55] 'To remove the influence of religion from public policy simply because some are uncomfortable with any degree of moral restraint is like the passenger on a sinking ship who removes his life jacket because it is restrictive and uncomfortable.'[56]"

Aaron could feel his own frustration building and added, "It has gone further than I ever thought possible. We have court orders that have falsely declared it unconstitutional to pray in school or at public meetings[57] or to display the Ten Commandments in schools[58] and other government buildings.[59] It has been taken even as far as declaring it unconstitutional for a person to have a cross-shaped planter in a public cemetery,[60] for a teacher to be seen at school with a copy of the Bible,[61] and for nativity scenes to be displayed on public property.[62] 'Although states print hundreds of thousands of custom license plates purchased and ordered by individual citizens, Oregon refused to print, 'PRAY,'[63] Virginia refused to print, 'GOD 4 US,'[64] and Utah refused to print, 'THANK GOD,'[65] claiming that such customized license plates violated the 'separation of church and state.'[66]"

Jefferson sighed heavily and shook his head. "No words of mine ever supported such things, but it is easy for me to see why they are so actively trying to remove God from government. In order to set up a socialistic government, you must first remove God. Karl Marx, author of the Communist Manifesto, declared, 'The first requisite is the abolition of religion. My object in life is to dethrone God.'[67] Socialists attempt to set themselves up as gods to rule and reign as masters over their adjuncts. Many are trying to remove God from government through the fabricated disguise of 'separation of church and state' so they can then set themselves up as masters. The basic concept of socialism is that the government has the full responsibility for the welfare of its citizens, and in order to fulfill that responsibility, it must assume control of all their activities. Under socialism, human rights are not granted by God, but by the government.

"'Let us consider the origin of those freedoms we have come to know as human rights. There are only two possible sources. Rights are either God-given as part of the divine plan, or they are granted by government as part of the political plan. Reason, necessity, tradition, and religious convictions all lead me to accept the divine origin of these rights. If we accept the premise that human rights are granted by government, then we must be willing to accept the corollary that they can be denied by government. I, for one, shall never accept that premise.'[68] 'Can the liberties of a nation be thought secure when we have removed their only firm basis, a conviction in the minds of the people that these liberties are . . . the gift of God? That they are not to be violated but with His wrath?'[69]"

Jefferson walked toward Aaron, coming to a stop at his side. He began sketching a tree on a piece of paper. "This illustration can depict the differences between a constitutional democratic republic and socialism.

"In a constitutional democratic republic, our Creator is represented as the roots of the tree. From the roots of God spring the God-given rights of life, liberty, and the pursuit of happiness. These are represented as the tree trunk of liberty and choice. Government is illustrated as a protective fence with an armed soldier, separate from the tree. The government is created by the people to protect the God-given rights of life, liberty, and the pursuit of happiness.

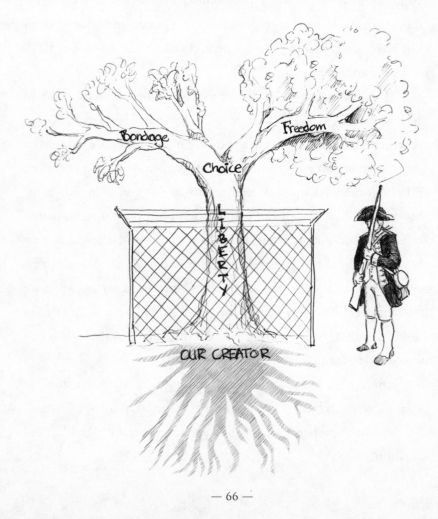

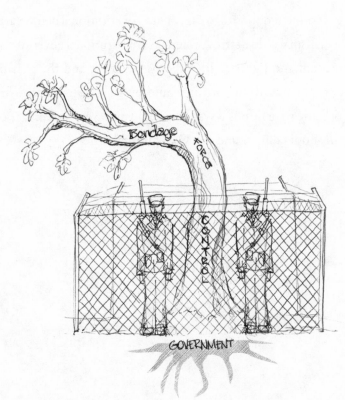

"In socialism, the government is represented as the roots of the tree. Socialism and communism are often referred to as godless, because under socialism and communism, government replaces God. God-given rights are replaced by the dictates of the government. The government is not created to protect God-given rights, but to control and force the citizens to live by its dictates. The tree trunk of control and force, as well as the prison fence with guards preventing escape, represent this."

Jefferson's voice rose in power and volume as he declared, "Socialism is not a political plan or party under the American Constitution. It is a system of government opposite to that of our constitutional democratic republic. Socialism would destroy America's constitutional government and our freedom and rights to life, liberty, property, and the pursuit of happiness. No American patriot would ever support a socialistic program, because socialism is a system of human slavery and an act of treason against our country and our God-given liberties."

CHAPTER 9:

PILLAR 2—DIVINE LAWS AND LAWS TO PROTECT GOD-GIVEN RIGHTS

Aaron was struck by the power and force of Jefferson's statement. There was a moment of silence as Jefferson left his illustration with Aaron and returned to his seat at the table. He took his seat and said, "Recognizing God-given rights does little good if there is not a system to protect these rights. 'A wise and frugal government, which shall restrain men from injuring one another'[70] is necessary to make a happy and prosperous people. My dear friend John Adams will teach you pillar two of the Constitution: divine laws and laws to protect God-given rights. John 'was honest as a politician as well as a man.'[71] He is a man of great integrity, who 'supported the Declaration with zeal and ability, fighting fearlessly for every word of it.'[72] John 'was the ablest advocate and champion of independence . . . he came out with a power which moved his hearers from their seats.'[73]"

President Washington rose to his feet and continued Jefferson's introduction of John Adams, "Thomas and John were a great team in the fight for independence. While Thomas was the author of the Declaration of Independence, John was the chief advocate on the floor of Congress. Thomas was the pen and John was the voice of independence. In life, they were friends for over fifty years, and in death, they were not separated. John and Thomas passed away on the fiftieth anniversary of the Declaration of Independence in 1826. When John was asked if he had a message for the fiftieth celebration of the fourth, he declared, 'Independence Forever.'[74] John and Thomas lived to see the expanded greatness and consolidated strength of a pure republic. They died amid the hosannas and grateful benedictions of a numerous, happy, and joyful people. Their passing together on the Fourth of July was not a mere coincidence but was a visible manifestation of Divine favor and a witness that our country and its citizens are under God's care. Thomas's last words on earth were fitting for this man of faith and service: 'I resign myself to my God, and my child to my country.'[75] John is a man of honor whose faith in God is firm and unshakable. Officiating at his funeral Pastor Peter Whitney declared, 'He died in good old age, full of days . . . and honor.'[76]"

Washington turned to John and nodded as to indicate it was his turn to speak. John Adams was sitting between Washington and Jefferson, and as he stood up, he said, "Thomas Jefferson was 'one of the choice ones of the earth.'[77] He then turned, and looking directly at Jefferson, said, "My friendship with you was 'one of the most agreeable events in my life.'[78]"

He turned his gaze to Aaron and began to speak. "The phrase 'all men are created equal' is a profound truth found in America's founding documents. 'All men are born free and equal'[79] and there are divine laws which affect everyone the same regardless of race, age, or gender. Each divine law creates a choice to obey or disobey. With each choice, comes a divinely appointed consequence. No amount of rationalizing or complaining will alter the consequence. If you pick up one end of a stick (choice), you also pick up the other end of the stick (the consequence of that choice). Divine laws, such as gravity, govern our lives. A child, though ignorant of the law, will still fall if he jumps off a ledge. The laws that govern wealth, health, and relationships are as clear and as binding as those that govern the earth. Regardless of whether or not we know or understand the laws, they always operate the same. Our success or failure, our happiness or unhappiness, depends on our knowledge and application of these laws in our lives.

"As we obey divine laws, we move to a more successful state of happiness, peace, power, freedom, and prosperity. As we disobey the laws, we move to a state of sadness, weakness, bondage, and misery. Each moment we are progressing toward one of these two states. The gift of choice is like fire: if properly used, it creates warmth and life; if improperly used, it can burn or even kill.

"On a farm, you reap what you sow. If you plant corn, you harvest corn. Similarly, we reap what we sow in life. Our choices are the seeds and the consequences the harvest. Just as a farmer cannot plant corn and harvest wheat, we cannot eliminate or change the consequences of our choices."

Aaron had several examples come to his mind and said, "In our society today, we see many who seek to eliminate the consequences of bad choices. There are those who smoke cigarettes and then want the government to provide health care to treat their lung cancer. There are those who have incurred large amounts of debt and then seek to be delivered from the obligation of repayment through bankruptcy, forcing someone else to pay their debts. There are those who seek deliverance from a disease of choice by taking a pill to treat the problem instead of changing the behavior that causes the problem."

"Great examples," Adams replied. "We must accept responsibility, which is the willingness and ability to recognize and accept the consequences of our actions. We have all heard someone describe freedom as having no laws, saying, 'No one can tell me what to do. I am in charge of my own life. Divine laws are restrictive and to be free one must not be bound by God's laws.' However, divine laws do not limit liberty; they provide a road map to joy and freedom. The violation of God's laws lead to bondage, pain, and misery.

"For example, two people are looking for a place to swim when they come upon a sign that reads, 'Danger! Whirlpool—No Swimming Allowed.' Both of these people have the liberty to choose whether to swim here or not. One swimmer chooses to enter the water and is sucked in. Because of his choice; he is now in bondage to the whirlpool. The other person chooses not to enter the water, and as a result, has the freedom to find another place to swim. Freedom results when we use our liberty correctly. Bondage results when we use our liberty incorrectly. The correct use of liberty—the power to choose—will result in more choices. The misuse of our liberty will result in fewer choices. Each time we make a choice we either gain more freedom as a result of our increased choices, or we digress toward bondage as the result of our diminished choices.

"'If someone decides to rob a bank, for instance, he or she may be incarcerated under the law. That person not only loses the ability to rob banks but is also restricted from other lawful activities in the future. A trip to the park, while lawful, is no longer an option after incarceration. The opposite is also true. If you choose to open a bank and work hard within the boundaries of the law, you can continue that activity and will have opportunities you did not have previously. A lawful and successful enterprise would provide funding for additional activities that you could not afford before your choice to provide banking services.'[80]

"All men and women are born equal but then become unequal as they make decisions. Everyone chooses to obey divine laws differently. One may choose to be idle while another may choose to build a business. One may choose to turn on the television while another may choose to read an uplifting book. One may choose to golf on his day off while another chooses to spend time with family. One may choose to listen to the radio on the way to work while another may choose to listen to audio books. We are born equal, yet years later we live diversely, all because we chose to live divine laws differently.

"Laws are to be created and enforced to assist us in living in accordance with divine law and to protect our God-given rights. John Locke taught, 'The end of law is not to abolish or restrain, but to preserve and enlarge freedom.'[81] Many have wondered what literature we used to assist us in the formation of the new government. We studied numerous historians, philosophers, economists, lawyers, and the Holy Bible. We drew upon the writing of Montesquieu, a French writer famous for his theory on the separation of powers. To assist us in developing law, William Blackstone, an English jurist and professor who wrote the book Commentaries on the Laws of England, was a very helpful resource, and John Locke, an English philosopher who developed the concepts of 'government with the consent of the governed' and the 'rights of life, liberty, and property,' was also used. However, the most frequently cited book in the founding literature was the Bible.[82] In all that we did, we sought to have the inspiration and direction of God in our work to ensure our laws aligned with the divine laws that lead to success.

"'Our Constitution was made only for a moral and religious people. It is wholly inadequate to the government of any other.'[83] 'We must never forget that nations may, and usually do, sow the seeds of their own destruction while enjoying unprecedented prosperity. . . At least twenty great civilizations have disappeared. The pattern is shockingly similar. All, before their collapse, showed a decline in spiritual values, in moral stamina, and in the freedom and responsibility of their citizens . . . [divine laws] are the foundational principles upon which all civilized government and our present civilization is built. To disregard them will lead to inevitable personal character loss and ruin. To disregard them as a nation will inevitably lead that nation to destruction.'[84]"

Aaron said, "This reminds me of one of my favorite quotes. May I share it with the group?" Adams nodded in the affirmative, and Aaron continued, "The famous French historian Alexis de Tocqueville traveled to America in the early 1800s to find out what made America great. He said of his experience, 'I sought for the greatness and genius of America in her commodious harbors and her ample rivers, and it was not there; in her fertile fields and boundless prairies, and it was not there; in her rich mines and her vast world of commerce, and it was not there. Not until I went to the churches of America and heard her pulpits aflame with righteousness did I understand the secret of her genius and power.

America is great because she is good, and if America ever ceases to be good, America will cease to be great.'[85]"

"Thank you." Adams replied, "That is a great summary and conclusion to our discussion on divine law.

CHAPTER 10:

DELIVERY OF THE ENVELOPES

Paula listened to the radio and tried to relax as she drove toward Langley. It was a beautiful sunny day, and as she crossed over the Keys Bridge, she could see many boats on the Potomac River. After crossing, she merged onto the George Washington Memorial Parkway, which ran along the river and was lined with trees on both sides. Her favorite song began playing on the radio and she sang along, enjoying the scenic drive. It felt nice to momentarily escape the modern Washington D.C. area, which, today, felt like it was filled with a pack of wolves stalking prey.

Traffic was light with just a few cars on the highway around her. Suddenly a large black SUV appeared to Paula's immediate left. It quickly closed the space between them and slammed into the driver's side of her car.

The impact from the hit forced her from the road. As she hit the shoulder, she jerked the steering wheel sharply to the left, desperately trying to get back on the road, causing the car to roll. The car did one complete tumble, crushing the sides and roof and shattering all the windows. The car came to rest on its tires near the river. At the site of the crash, there was a clearing with no trees between the parkway and the river.

Paula had been knocked unconscious, and the SUV pulled swiftly off the road in front of Paula's car. A man jumped out of the SUV, rushed to the car, and grabbed the bag from the floor of the front seat. He opened the bag to find the envelopes she had gathered. He then came to the driver's side of the car, placed the car into neutral, and gave the car a push down the hill toward the river. The man sprinted to his SUV and sped off, leaving Paula to drown in the river.

The car splashed head on into the river and began drifting with the current, sinking slowly. A man coming up the parkway saw the car slide into the water. He pulled to the side of the road, ran to the river and jumped in. He swam out to the car, which was almost completely submersed, and dove under water to the driver's side window.

The roof was smashed, but the windows were still big enough to pull the body of the unconscious driver from the sinking tomb. He reached in through the window, unbuckled the seat belt, and pulled her from the car. He trudged them both out of the water and up onto the bank.

He checked for a pulse and found one, but she was not breathing. The man tilted Paula's head slightly back, pinched her nose, sealed his mouth over hers, and breathed four strong breaths into her lungs, but there was still no response. He repeated this sequence a second time with no result.

After his third set of breaths, Paula began coughing up water. He turned her head to the side and allowed the water to drain. Soon she began breathing on her own and started coming to consciousness. The man did not detect any major injures. It appeared she had survived the crash with only a few bruises.

Paula heard the sound of sporadic applause around her. Still working to regain all her senses, she blinked her eyes several times and looked around to see a small crowd of bystanders surrounding her. Looking up, her eyes were met by the warm, brown eyes of a man she had never met before. She slowly realized that her head was being cradled on his lap, his hands checking her pulse and clearing her wet hair away from her face.

Suddenly her last few moments of consciousness came back to her, and panic set in. "Where's my car? Where's my purse?" Paula had an image in her mind of the envelopes resting at the bottom of the river.

An elderly woman in the small group that was gathered around Paula couldn't help but comment, "I saw the whole thing. Your purse is long gone. The man from the SUV that forced you off the road took your purse and then pushed your car into the river. While I was calling 911, he..." she nodded at the man holding Paula, "seemed to come out of nowhere, jumped into the water, and saved your life."

As she looked up at the man, Paula said, "Thank you for saving my life."

The man replied, "You're welcome. Just doing my job."

"Doing your job? What's your job?" Paula asked.

The man replied, "I'm Special Agent Stanley Johnson with the FBI."

"Stanley Johnson." Paula repeated aloud. She knew that name. It came to her with a jolt.

"Stanley Johnson," she said again, "I was just coming to see you!"

"Why were you coming to see me?"

"I'm the chief of staff for Vice President Banner. He asked me to give you something."

Agent Johnson replied, "Let's get you to a secure location at FBI Headquarters. You can fill me in on the way." Agent Johnson helped Paula to her feet and walked her to his car.

As they drove to FBI Headquarters, Paula told Agent Johnson of her meeting with Vice President Banner a week earlier and about the letter he had given her. Paula then said, "Vice President Banner hid five envelopes containing information regarding crimes committed by various members of the government. The letter asked me to get these five envelopes and deliver them to five people Vice President Banner trusted—one of them being you, Agent Johnson."

Agent Johnson replied, "So were you able to get all of the envelopes."

"All but one of them," Paula answered. "It appears to me that someone beat me to the one that was inside Vice President Banner's wall safe. I found the other four and was on my way to deliver the first of them at Langley when, well you know the rest of the story."

Agent Johnson asked, "Do you know what was in the envelopes? Are there any others?"

Paula answered, "I don't know what was inside those envelopes. I only know it was information that would expose those involved in various crimes. Sorry I couldn't be of more help, but that's all I know."

"So there are no more hidden envelopes?"

"No. All of the envelopes I retrieved were in my purse. But, a week ago, when Vice President Banner gave me the envelope with instructions to open it only if he was harmed, he also gave me a package and asked me to hide it in a secure location known only to me. He didn't give me any other instructions regarding the package."

"Well, it looks like this is our last hope of finding out what people are willing to kill for and who is involved. Where is the package hidden?"

"It's in my office," Paula answered.

"We are only a few minutes from the Eisenhower Building. Let's stop by your office, get this package, and take it with us to the FBI," Agent Johnson suggested.

Paula nodded her head in agreement, but she didn't want to speak as the reality of this heinous day weighed upon her. They rode in silence for a couple of minutes. As they neared the Eisenhower Building, Agent Johnson saw smoke billowing from one of the windows and exclaimed, "The building's on fire."

Paula quickly looked up to see dark smoke pouring from one window and said, "The smoke appears to be coming from my office."

Agent Johnson asked, "Where did you hide the package? We must save it from the fire."

Paula began to respond, but then paused as if something had stopped her. Agent Johnson impatiently demanded, "Where did you hide the package?"

"In the wood filing cabinet," Paula stumbled over her answer, "in the second drawer from the bottom, mixed in with the papers in the file marked 'Past Calendars.'"

The fire department and other response teams had not yet arrived. Agent Johnson pulled right in front of the building, grabbed a blanket and gloves from the back seat, and got out of the car where he was immediately met by security.

Agent Johnson flashed his badge. "I'm with the FBI," he said, his voice rushed. "I need to get in there now!" The guard waved him through, and Agent Johnson rushed into the building against the flowing tide of people rushing out. Agent Johnson ran into the nearest bathroom, quickly soaking his gloves and blanket with water from the toilets. He threw the blanket around his shoulders as he continued his dash up the stairs.

He arrived at the room and found most of the room's exterior engulfed in flames but there was still a path through the room to the wood filing cabinet. The drawer of the cabinet slid out easily. He didn't have time to rifle through the files as the flames surrounding him were growing rapidly, and his exposed skin felt as if it would soon begin to melt under the intense heat.

Agent Johnson took a satchel that he had carried with him into the building, pulled out a small container of gasoline, and dumped it onto the files in the drawer. He grabbed an item in the room that was on fire and ignited the files. He watched for a moment from the hallway to make sure the files and cabinet would be completely destroyed.

As he turned from the room to exit the building, the entire cabinet was engulfed in flames. His job was complete. He now knew all the information Vice President Banner had hidden was destroyed. Paula had collected all the envelopes for them and confirmed this package to be the last of them. Earlier in the day, a member of his team had retrieved the file from the Vice President's wall safe.

Agent Johnson left the building to see that the fire department had just arrived and were hoisting their ladders and preparing to enter the burning office.

"Did you find the file and package?" Paula asked as Agent Johnson entered the car.

"I was too late," Agent Johnson replied. "The whole room was filled with flames and there was no way to get to the cabinet. I'm sorry."

Agent Johnson and Paula drove down the street to FBI Headquarters where Paula was taken to a room to be debriefed.

CHAPTER 11:

PILLAR 3—LIMITED POWER GRANTED BY THE PEOPLE

John Adams concluded his remarks saying, "There has to be laws to protect our God-given rights, but the government's power to protect our rights has to be limited. 'The only maxim of a free government ought to be to trust no man living with power to endanger the public liberty.'[86] This leads us to pillar three of the Constitution—limited power granted by the people."

Aaron was amazed at the instruction and council he was receiving from the heroes of American history. It was exciting for him to see that these great patriots and advocates for freedom continued to support the cause of freedom.

Adams sat down, and George Washington began to introduce the next person to speak. "This man lived and died a patriot. His father, John, was a soldier in the Revolutionary War, [87] and he wanted to serve his country as well. He was a congressional representative from the state of Tennessee for six years, and he took seriously his oath of office to 'support the Constitution of the United States.'[88]

"On October 31, 1835, he left Tennessee for Texas to help in its fight for freedom. He arrived at the Alamo on February 8, 1836. The thirteen-day battle of the Alamo began February 23. The Alamo forces only consisted of approximately two hundred patriots. On the other hand, by the end of the twelfth day of battle, the Mexican forces attacking the post were reported to be more than four thousand. He fought courageously and echoed the words of his commander, Lt. Col. William B. Travis, who wrote in his final dispatch, 'The enemy has demanded a surrender at discretion, otherwise the garrison are to be put to the sword if the fort is taken. I have answered the demand with a cannon shot, and our flag still waves proudly from the walls. I shall never surrender or retreat . . . I am determined to sustain myself as long as possible and die like a soldier who never forgets what is due to his own honor and that of his country. Victory or Death!'[89]

"The small band of two hundred patriots was able to hold off the Mexican army for thirteen days, delaying their movement eastward. This gave the Texan revolutionaries more time to gather troops and supplies, which led to a decisive defeat of the Mexican forces at the Battle of San Jacinto on April 21, 1836, and to the establishment of the independent Republic of Texas. In life, Davy Crockett fought to preserve the freedoms of the US Constitution and at age forty-nine he made the ultimate sacrifice by giving his life in the Battle of the Alamo. Davy Crockett lived and died a patriot.[90]"

Davy Crockett rose to his feet saying, "There are many at this table much more qualified to speak than I am. I studied the lives and teachings of many of the men at this table during my service as a member of the US House of Representatives. Aaron, I have been asked to share a story from my time as a congressman that teaches some of the principles of limited government.

"One winter evening while standing on the steps of the Capitol, I and other members of congress saw, as the result of a large fire, great light coming from Georgetown. We rode over as fast as we could. When we got there, I went to work, but in spite of all that could be done, many houses were burned and many families made homeless. Some of them had lost all but the clothes they had on. The next morning, a bill was introduced appropriating $20,000 (which would be approximately $400,000 in today's dollars) for their relief. We put aside all other business and rushed it through as soon as it could be done.

"The following summer, while working for reelection, I stopped to talk with a farmer in one of my districts. The man turned to his plow and was about to start off when I said, 'Don't be in such a hurry, my friend, I want to have a little talk with you and get better acquainted.' The man replied, 'Yes, I know you; you are Colonel Crockett... I shall not vote for you again.'

"I asked what was the matter, to which the man replied, 'You gave a vote last winter which shows that either you have not capacity to understand the Constitution, or that you are wanting in the honesty and firmness to be guided by it. In either case you are not the man to represent me. If the Constitution is to be worth anything, it must be held sacred and rigidly observed in all its provisions.'

"I replied, 'I admit the truth of all you say, but there must be some mistake about it, for I do not remember that I gave any vote last winter upon any constitutional question.' The man answered, 'No, Colonel, there's no mistake. Last winter you voted for a bill to appropriate $20,000 to some sufferers by a fire in Georgetown. Is that true?'

"I answered, 'Well, my friend, I may as well own up. You have got me there. But certainly nobody will complain that a great and rich country likes ours should give the insignificant sum of $20,000 to relieve its suffering women and children, particularly with a full and overflowing treasury, and I am sure, if you had been there, you would have done just as I did.'

"The man responded, 'It is not the amount, Colonel, that I complain of—it is the principle... The power of collecting and disbursing money at pleasure is the most dangerous power that can be entrusted to man . . . you see, that while you are contributing to relieve one, you are drawing it from thousands . . . Colonel, Congress has no right to give charity. Individual members may give as much of their own money as they please, but they have no right to touch a dollar of the public money for that purpose . . . The people have delegated to Congress, by the Constitution, the power to do certain things. To do these, it is authorized to collect and pay moneys, and for nothing else. Everything beyond this is usurpation, and a violation of the Constitution. . . So you see, Colonel, you have violated the Constitution in what I consider a vital point. It is a precedent fraught with danger to the country, for when Congress once begins to stretch its power beyond the limits of the Constitution, there is no limit to it, and no security for the people.'

"Realizing the man was right, I replied, 'Well, my friend, you hit the nail upon the head when you said I did not have sense enough to understand the Constitution. I intended to be guided by it, and thought I had studied it fully. If I had ever taken the view of it that you have, I would have put my head into the fire before I would have given that vote, and . . . if I ever vote for another unconstitutional law I wish I may be shot.'

"Following this experience, a bill was raised to appropriate money to the widow of a distinguished naval officer. Several beautiful speeches were made in its support. It appeared the bill would pass unanimously when I arose and spoke. 'Mr. Speaker—I have as much respect for the memory of the deceased, and as much sympathy for the suffering of the living. I will not go into an argument to prove that Congress has no power to appropriate this money as an act of charity. Every member upon this floor knows it. We have the right, as individuals, to give away as much of our own money as we please to charity; but as members of Congress we have no right to appropriate a dollar of the public money. We cannot, without the grossest corruption, appropriate this money. We have not the semblance of authority to appropriate it as charity. I cannot vote for this bill, but I will give one week's pay to the object, and, if every member of Congress will do the same, it will amount to more than the bill asks.'[91] As a result of my speech, the bill failed, receiving very few votes. I had honored my oath to 'support the Constitution.'"

The others at the table began to share their ideas and experience on limiting government power. James Madison declared, "If the government was to 'assume the provision of the poor . . . it would subvert the very foundations and transmute the very nature of the limited government established by the people of America.'[92] For every give-away program the government implements, it has to create an even greater take-away program to pay for it, for 'nothing can enter the public treasury for the benefit of one citizen or one class unless other citizens and other classes have been forced to send it in.'[93]

"'When a portion of wealth is transferred from the person who owns it—without his consent and without compensation, and whether by force or by fraud—to anyone who does not own it, then I say that property is violated; that an act of plunder is committed . . . How is this legal plunder to be identified? Quite simply. See if the law takes from some persons what belongs to them, and gives it to other persons to whom it does not belong. See if the law benefits one citizen at the expense of another by doing what the citizen himself cannot do without committing a crime.'[94] Unfortunately, the US Constitution, designed to protect peoples' rights and property, has now been twisted, misinterpreted, and changed to become a system of legal plunder through the many redistribution programs operated by the government. This should shock the conscience of every American. For 'it is impossible to introduce into society . . . a greater evil than this: the conversion of the law into an instrument of plunder.'[95]"

George Washington then added, "'The sole object and only legitimate end of government is to protect the citizen in the enjoyment of life, liberty, and property, and when the government assumes other functions it is usurpation and oppression.'[96] Government is not to rule the people—the people are to rule the government. The Declaration of Independence reads, 'to secure these rights, governments are instituted among men, deriving their just powers from the consent of the governed . . .' The preamble of the US Constitution states, 'We, the people of the United States ... do ordain and establish this Constitution.' The Constitution established a form of government described as 'of the people, by the people, and for the people.' We must oppose any action by government that oversteps the bounds of the limited power given to it by the people to protect the rights of the citizens."

Benjamin Franklin added, "As the government has overstepped its constitutional bounds, the spending of the government has ballooned. I see many in your day that are carrying a heavy burden of taxes, which has been placed on their backs by unconstitutional programs. Aaron, the tax burden your people face today far exceeds the tax burden from Britain that the colonies sought relief from. To reduce the great tax burden on your people, you must reduce the size and scope of government. If the federal government only provides the services authorized by the Constitution, the spending and cost to Americans would be a very small fraction of what it is today. Now, a word of warning, if the current trends of government growth and the increase of government redistribution are not reversed, America will no longer be the land of the free and home of the brave, but will be the land of the slaves and home of the dependants. Action must be taken to freeze the growth and phase out all redistribution programs until the limited government created by the inspired Constitution is restored."

Thomas Jefferson continued, "One way the Constitution limits power is by separating it. The Constitution separates the power of government between the national, state, and local governments, and divides the national government into three branches: legislative, executive, and judicial. 'The way to have good and safe government is not to trust it all to one, but to divide it among the many, distributing to every one exactly the functions he is competent to. Let the national government be entrusted with the defense of the nation, and its foreign and federal relations; the state governments with the civil rights, law, police, and administration of what concerns the state generally; the counties with the local concerns of the counties, and each township direct the interests within itself . . . What has destroyed liberty and the rights of man in every government which has ever existed under the sun? The generalizing and concentrating all cares and powers into one body."[97]

"As the Constitution has been violated and power has become more and more centralized with the Federal government, the independence and power of the states has been eroded, as has the freedom of each of the citizens of these states. One of the beauties of independent states joined together for national defense is the element of competition between the states. If one state were to place a heavy burden of tax on its people, they could go to a neighboring state with lower taxes. The independent states and free movement by the citizens between the states provides a check and balance and prevents state governments from violating the state constitutions and the power granted them by the people. When power is centralized with the Federal government who has power over all the states, this advantage is lost and eventually freedom is also lost. We want to again be fifty independent states that are the United States of America. There is to be fifty independent states united for national trade and defense. It must be remembered that the states created the federal government, and thus the federal government should be controlled and directed by the states, not the other way around."

Washington concluded the discussion on limited government. "'Government is . . . like fire, it is a dangerous servant and a fearful master; never for a moment should it be left to irresponsible action.'"[98]

'The history of liberty is a history of limitations of governmental power, not the increase of it ... concentration of power is what always precedes the destruction of human liberty.'[99]

CHAPTER 12:
THE LAST PACKAGE

Paula sat in a room at FBI Headquarters waiting for someone to come and interview her. After waiting a few minutes, an agent entered the room and asked her to relate the events of the day. She began with a detailed account of her meeting with Vice President Banner last week. She then explained how she had secured all but one of the envelopes and was attempting to deliver these envelopes when she was run off the road into the Potomac River, had the envelopes stolen from her, and then was rescued by Agent Johnson. She then related how Agent Johnson had tried, unsuccessfully, to recover the package from her burning office.

The FBI interviewer asked, "Is there anything else?"

Paula shook her head no, and the interviewer seemed to be satisfied and got up to leave the room.

Paula asked, "So, am I free to go?"

The interviewer replied, "I would suggest you stay in protective custody, but yes, you are free to go if you wish. We will get in touch with you should we have any further questions."

Paula was relieved the interviewer seemed satisfied that she did not have any more information, since she had not shared the entire truth with him. When Agent Johnson asked her for the location of the package hidden in her office, she heard a distinct voice from the Holy Spirit say, "Do not give him the location of the package." As a result of this prompting, Paula felt certain that Agent Johnson was somehow involved in the cover-up and could not be trusted, so she gave him a false location for the package.

She had placed the package inside a metal box in a secret compartment of her office floor near her desk. She was confident that the box would have protected the package from the fire. How was she going to get the package, though, and to whom should she give it? After the betrayal of Agent Johnson, she was not sure whom she could trust.

Paula knew she needed divine direction, so she prayed over the four remaining names, Eric Fisher, Associate Attorney General; Charles Morell, Deputy Director of the National Clandestine Service; Josh Wilson, CIA Agent; and Jacob Pryor, Senator—the names given to her by Vice President Banner to see which of these she could trust with this valuable package.

Charles Morell came to her mind. When Paula said his name, she felt at peace. Charles Morell would be the one to help her. She went to the ladies' room hoping that there was no video or audio surveillance there and called one of the receptionists at the White House.

She asked to be connected to Charles Morell's office. She announced herself to Morell's secretary as the chief of staff for Vice

President Banner, and that she had an urgent and important matter to speak to the Director about.

The secretary interrupted Charles' meeting to let him know he had an urgent phone call she thought he would want to take. He excused himself as the receptionist explained that the chief of staff for Vice President Banner, Paula Bracket, was on the line.

Charles went to his office, and the receptionist transferred the call to him.

"Hello Paula, this is Charles Morell."

"Thank you for taking my call," Paula replied.

Charles continued, "I heard on the news that you were in a serious car accident and that there was a fire at your office. Are you okay?"

"Yes. I'm fine, but I really need your help in regards to things that have happened to Vice President Banner and me today. Can you meet me right now at my office in the Eisenhower Building?"

This was definitely out of the ordinary, but nothing that day had been ordinary. Charles's gut was telling him he needed to go meet her. He answered, "I can be there in fifteen minutes."

"Thank you, Charles. I'll explain more when you arrive."

They each hung up the phone. Charles headed to his car, and Paula exited the bathroom. She no longer had a car, so she would need to make the one mile trip to her office on foot. If she walked quickly, she would arrive at her office around the same time as Charles.

She was nervous to leave the security of the Federal Building, but those involved in the crimes and cover-up now believed that they had all the envelopes, and that she had no incriminating knowledge. She felt she would no longer be a target or at risk—unless they somehow became aware of her call and meeting with Charles Morell.

The words from her prayer earlier in the day were brought to her remembrance. "Please prepare and guide my path and protect me from harm. Please frustrate the efforts of those fighting against us and obscure my efforts from their view." She felt a peace come over her that God was indeed guiding and protecting her, and that her efforts with Charles were being obscured from evil's view by the Divine Hand of Providence.

Paula did not look forward to the walk to the Eisenhower Building. She was tired, in pain, and felt her breathing restrained by the water in her lungs. However, she knew she must press on. As she walked along the sidewalks, it appeared to her that most of the people she passed on the streets were carrying on as normal. She hoped her life would soon be back to that state as well, but she knew that today was a pivotal day in history and in her life.

America would never be the same. It took her about fifteen minutes to arrive in front of the office building. Although the fire had been put out, the building still remained evacuated and surrounded by fire trucks and police cars.

Paula entered the building and was permitted through security. When she reached her office she found several firemen inside, and as she tried to enter, she was stopped by one of them. "We're still working here. No one should be in this room or the building, for that matter."

"This is my office," Paula answered, "and I would really appreciate it if you would just let me come in for one minute, and then I'll be out of your way."

"The building is structurally sound, so I guess I can let you in," the firefighter replied. "You've got sixty seconds to get what you need."

Paula thanked him and went toward what was left of her now burnt desk. It appeared to her that the fire had destroyed almost everything in her office. She hoped she would be able to get the package from the box without drawing attention. The firefighter had gone back to work and, for the moment, appeared to be paying no attention to her. She opened the hidden compartment in the floor near her desk and pulled out the metal box.

She held her breath as she opened the lid and immediately let out a sigh of relief. "Thank you, Lord," Paula said silently. The package had been undisturbed by the fire. Paula placed the package in her bag and returned the box to its hiding place in the floor.

As she exited the room, she spotted Charles coming down the hallway. She quickly walked toward him. "Follow me, Charles," she said as she motioned him to follow her to the women's bathroom—a room which had neither video nor audio surveillance. As they entered the bathroom, Paula began to speak. "Thank you for coming, Charles. You may be one of the only people I can trust today, and I desperately need help."

"What's going on? And what can I do?" Charles replied.

Paula took a deep breath and began recounting the alarming series of events that had led her to having a secret meeting in the women's bathroom with a member of the National Clandestine Service. "A week ago, Vice President Banner gave me an envelope with instructions to open it should anything happen to him. After he was shot this morning, I opened the letter to find that the Vice President had discovered information on crimes and cover-ups by several individuals within the government. The letter asked me to recover five hidden envelopes, which contained information to bring these corrupt individuals to justice. He then asked me to deliver these envelopes to people in the FBI, CIA, and Justice Department.

The envelopes were stolen by the people that tried to drown me in the Potomac River. The man that pulled me from the river was FBI Special Agent Stanley Johnson. I don't think it was a coincidence that he was at the scene of my crash so quickly. He did save my life, but I believe he's working with the enemy, and wanted to make sure they had destroyed all the evidence against them. In addition to these five envelopes, Vice President Banner also gave me a package to hide.

I told Agent Johnson about this last package but gave him a false location for it. I think he believes the package was destroyed in my office fire. What I am about to give you may be the last remaining evidence of the corruption Vice President Banner uncovered. After my interaction with Special Agent Johnson, I truly did not know who I could trust to help me. As I prayed over the remaining four names that the Vice President gave me, your name kept coming to my mind. God trusts you, so I know I can trust you."

Paula pulled the package from her bag and handed it to Charles. He opened the package to find a jump drive. Even though neither of them knew what was on the jump drive, they could each feel the magnitude of importance the data on this tiny device must contain.

"Paula, I will ensure this information is secure," Charles said. "Once I've reviewed the data, I promise I'll do what needs to be done."

Paula felt a sense of relief. She had accomplished the task Vice President Banner had entrusted to her and, for now, felt that her job was complete. She felt a peace and assurance that Charles would be able to take the information and finish this perilous assignment.

"I'll be praying for you and your safety, Charles. Let me know if there is anything else you need from me."

"Thank you, Paula. I'll let you know what I find out when I believe it's safe. I don't want to put you in harm's way again."

Charles and Paula parted ways and exited separately from the building. Since Charles was not sure whom he could trust at his office, he decided to take the jump drive to his home to analyze the data it contained.

As he drove to his home, he was on heightened awareness for anything out of the ordinary and carefully watched to see if he was being followed. He pulled into the driveway and opened the garage door confident that he wasn't followed. His wife's car was not in the garage, so he would have the house to himself. He walked inside, went to his office, and inserted the jump drive into the USB port of his computer.

As he began exploring the files on the drive, he was shocked to find emails, photos, videos, and audio files linking several individuals in government positions to numerous crimes. Charles quickly understood why such an effort had been made to recover this information. One email detailed a plan to manipulate electronic voting machines in an election. An audio file revealed a plot to hire an assassin to silence a potential whistle blower who had learned too much.

One file showed a clear money trail to government agencies that were making millions of dollars from illegal drug sales, while another file showed a series of campaign contributions and bribes to government officials in exchange for large government contracts and other political favors. Charles's heart sank as he read evidence of government officials providing a terrorist organization with information needed to plan and execute a terrorist attack on US citizens. There were a series of documents showing extensive corruption in starting and extending wars. War appeared to be a goose that provided many golden eggs for the powerful forces of evil that committed fraud, treason, and secret murders to proliferate war.

There were hundreds of files that would take days to read through, but he'd seen enough to know that his life would be in jeopardy should the powers of evil learn of the information he possessed. He looked inside one last folder on the drive titled "President of the United States" and found documents tying the current President, as well as some former Presidents, to the works of darkness and corruption revealed on this drive. Charles's heart weighed heavy with disappointment as he realized that many he had worked with over the years were revealed as traitors.

He knew he had to ensure this information was not destroyed, so he duplicated the information in various locations. He printed some of the content, burned information to CDs, made additional copies onto jump drives, and stored the data on two secure remote servers. Finished, he sat back in his chair and closed his eyes, letting the weight of the reality of what was happening rest upon him. He said a silent prayer for guidance and knowledge of what he should do next.

As he sat pondering, the Holy Spirit filled his body, and the thought came to his mind, "Meet with the Vice President of the United States."

"Impossible," he thought. "The Vice President is in a coma."

Again the powerful impression came, "Meet with the Vice President of the United States."

Charles felt a little perplexed, but his years of experience had taught him to trust God. He thought to himself, "God must know something I don't. If God wants me to meet with the Vice President of the United States, I'll meet with the Vice President of the United States."

Charles immediately called Paula to tell her about the information contained on the jump drive and the impression he had to meet with the Vice President. "Paula, I don't know how I'm supposed to meet with a man in a coma."

With excitement in her voice, Paula exclaimed, "This is great news! If you're to meet with the Vice President, that means he's going to live." Paula felt a sudden sense of confidence. "Sounds like for now we wait to talk to Vice President Banner. Our enemies think they've destroyed all the incriminating evidence, so we should be safe for now."

CHAPTER 13:

PILLAR 4—FREE ENTERPRISE

Washington transitioned to the fourth and final pillar of the Constitution by saying, "'Of all the founding fathers, Benjamin Franklin has the unique distinction of having signed all three of the major documents that freed the colonies from British rule and established the United States as an independent nation: the Declaration of Independence, the Treaty of Paris, and the United States Constitution.'[100]

"As a result of his success as a businessman, he became financially independent at the age of forty-two and was able to make many important contributions to society over the next forty-two years of his life as an author, inventor, philanthropist, and civil servant. 'The rise of Benjamin Franklin from modest beginnings to a station among the most accomplished Americans of his day has long been recognized as one of the world's great success stories.'[101] Franklin is the perfect individual to teach you about the fourth pillar of the Constitution: free enterprise."

Benjamin Franklin rose to his feet and spoke in a quiet yet powerful voice. "In creating a new form of government, we wanted to create an economic system that gave people the freedom to create, produce, and increase. 'The true foundation of republican government is the equal right of every citizen, in his person and property, and in their management. . . Our interest [was] to throw open the doors of commerce, and to knock off all its shackles, giving perfect freedom to all persons.'[102] Free enterprise 'offers the greatest opportunity for man to become what God intended.'[103] 'Some regard private enterprise as if it were a predatory tiger to be shot. Others look upon it as a cow that they can milk. Only a handful see it for what it really is—the strong horse that pulls the whole cart.'[104]"

Aaron was again impressed by the presentation skills of Franklin. As Franklin paused for a moment, Aaron spoke, "I agree wholeheartedly, yet there are still many who fight vigorously against free enterprise. Mr. Franklin, how do I combat the attacks on free enterprise?"

Franklin answered, "One attack on free enterprise is often expressed with the saying, 'the rich get richer, and the poor get poorer.' While this statement is monumentally wrong, many people seem to believe it. The truth is that the majority of those who are wealthy in America start out in poverty, as did I.[105 106] I spent the first years of my life in poverty, and 'America didn't give me a dole when I was broke, but she did give me some valuable assets—freedom and the opportunity to work.'[107 108]

"At age seventeen, I left Boston to go to Philadelphia for a fresh start. When I arrived on October 6, 1723, I was a broke runaway. To earn the money I needed to live, and to gain experience, I worked for several printers and merchants over the next five years. At age twenty-two, I decided it was time to start my own business, and I opened a printing shop. 'We had scarce . . . put our press in order, before George House, an acquaintance of mine, brought a countryman to us, who he had met in the street inquiring for a printer. . . This countryman's five shillings, being our first-fruits, and coming so seasonably, gave me more pleasure than any crown I have since earned.'[109]

"The opinion in the town was that my print shop would fail as there were already two printers in the place. I was determined to make it a success and worked hard to do a great job for my customers to win repeat and referral business. I also developed a profitable newspaper and the Poor Richard's Almanac.

"By the early 1730s, my business was thriving. I started to expand my business by sending young workers, once they had served their time with me, to set up partnership shops in places ranging from Charleston to Hartford. I would supply the presses and part of the expenses, as well as some content for the publications, and in return take a portion of the revenue.[110] Each year I worked to improve my condition, and by age forty-two, I was financially independent and considered rich. I went from the bottom level of income earners to the top level of income earners within a matter of years.[111] That is one of the great things about America. Everyone has the opportunity to create wealth and abundance."

Abraham Lincoln interjected, "'It is best for all to leave each man free to acquire property as fast as he can. Some will get wealthy. I don't believe in a law to prevent a man from getting rich; it would do more harm than good. . . When one starts poor, as most do in the race of life, free society is such that he knows he can better his condition. . . I am not ashamed to confess that . . . years ago I was a hired laborer. . . I want every man to have the chance . . . in which he can better his condition—when he may look forward and hope to be a hired laborer this year and the next, work for himself afterward, and finally to hire men to work for him. That is the true system. . . Property is the fruit of labor; property is desirable; is a positive good in the world. That some should be rich, shows that others may become rich, and hence is just encouragement to industry and enterprise. Let not him who is houseless pull down the house of another; but let him labor diligently and build one for himself.'[112]"

Franklin and Aaron nodded in agreement, and Franklin continued, "Aaron, another principle you must teach, which is essential to understanding free enterprise, is that the world is abundant. God created an earth that is designed to create, produce, and increase.[113] For example, from a single apple seed you can grow a tree that will produce hundreds of apples each year. Two chickens can be multiplied to feed thousands of people. The world is meant to be abundant, and God has given humans the unique ability to create resources rather than only use resources. Using our God-given ability to create resources is the key to our economic well-being.

"Now, there are many that teach scarcity—that there is a fixed amount of wealth. With a scarcity belief, if one person gains more financially it means another has less. A great example of a scarcity mentality is population control. There are those who want to limit the population because if there are more people, each person will get a smaller piece of the pie. With a scarcity mentality, the only way to increase the quality of life of each individual is to reduce the number of people. Thus, as population is reduced, each person receives a larger piece of the pie. Those who believe in scarcity will become angry with those who become rich, because they believe that since this person has more it means someone else now has less. Once it is understood that wealth can be created, it is understood that as we create wealth, we are improving the lives of society—not taking from it. A belief that the world is abundant and that wealth can be created is essential to creating a prosperous society. The more we develop an abundance mentality, the more we realize that the success of others adds to—rather than detracts from—our lives.[114]

"Aaron, when I breathe, does it lessen the amount of oxygen available for you and your family? Is the person who exercises and thus breathes more oxygen selfish because he is taking more than his share of the oxygen?"

Aaron replied to Franklin's questions, "Well, of course not. There is enough oxygen for everyone to breathe as much as they want."

Franklin then continued, "Why is there plenty of oxygen? Because oxygen can be created. Since oxygen is created in abundance, we don't have to ration it so we don't run out. Wealth can also be created and thus can be as abundant in our lives as oxygen. We can have as much wealth as we are willing to work to create. To say it is impossible for everyone to be wealthy is as irrational as saying not everyone can breathe as much oxygen as he or she wants. Once we understand that wealth can be created, we will believe that there is enough in the world for everyone to succeed. As a result, one does not have to become successful at the expense of others. The success of one does not limit another's ability to succeed.

"However, if you believe in scarcity and a fixed number of resources, you will focus on distributing the limited wealth among society fairly. You will not focus on creation because what currently exists is all there will ever be. Instead of trying to develop a way to divide the current pie, we should focus on creating new pies. If every person produced to his or her potential, everyone's needs would be satisfied with a great abundance. For example, the earth is capable of producing food for a population of at least eighty billion, eight times the ten billion expected to inhabit the earth by the year 2050. One study estimates that with improved scientific methods, the earth could feed as many as one thousand billion people.[115] In 1930, there were approximately thirty million farmers in the United States, barely producing enough food to feed a population of approximately one hundred million people. Technological breakthroughs in agriculture during the next fifty years made farming so efficient that by 1980 approximately three million farmers were producing enough food for a population of more than three hundred million. This represents a three thousand percent increase in productivity per farmer."[116]

Aaron raised his hand, and Franklin paused and nodded to give him permission to ask his question. Aaron asked, "I understand and believe what you are saying, but how do I answer the question, 'If the world is capable of feeding hundreds of billions of people, why are people starving?'"

"This is a great question," Franklin answered. "Remember that I said if every person produced to his or her potential, everyone's needs would be satisfied with a great abundance. There are several problems. First, most of the world does not have governments and economic systems that allow free enterprise. The United States is a powerful case study on the benefits of free enterprise. With less than five percent of the world's population,[117] the United States produces more than 28 percent of the world's goods and services.[118] The free enterprise system is superior by far to any economic system the world has ever known. America now has over three hundred million citizens, with a combined income of more than nine trillion dollars each year. There is clear evidence that as countries have implemented the principles of free enterprise, they have much higher levels of production and wealth. Second, not everyone is producing. Even in countries that have free enterprise, many people choose not to work. Third, there are those who seek wealth by taking what others have produced rather than creating it themselves. These are the three reasons we see areas of the world where production and wealth are far below what they could, and should, be."

Aaron nodded in agreement, and Franklin continued, "Another misconception you must correct is that the government can distribute wealth more fairly. Opponents to free enterprise can't ignore the fact that free enterprise creates more wealth than any other system, so they falsely claim that a socialist economy provides a more equal distribution of wealth. The opposite is actually true. Under socialism, all property and capital is owned and controlled by the government. As a result, the government leaders take a large share of the wealth before it is distributed to the citizens. Over time, this results in the government leaders holding most of the country's wealth."

"A study of socialist countries proves this fact," Aaron added, "'For example, the largest item of personal wealth in socialist nations is the automobile. In 1971, in the socialist countries of U.S.S.R and Poland, the top 1 percent of the population owned respectively 60 percent and 59 percent of the nation's automobiles. While in the US, the top 1 percent owned 3 percent of the nation's automobiles.'[119] Just as leaders in socialistic governments used their power to distribute a large portion of the nation's wealth to themselves, so have members of Congress in America. They are taking huge salaries, medical benefits, and retirement plans for a part-time job all at the expense of taxpayers. The Congress members' salaries are higher than 95% of the US population, and they have excluded themselves from paying into the socialist program of Social Security. They pay nothing into Social Security and yet receive millions in retirement benefits, while those who pay thousands of dollars into Social Security each year receive very meager retirement pay. Far from the equal distribution of wealth they promote and promise."

Franklin replied, "Great examples, Aaron. You are right that socialism results in the concentration of wealth with the government leaders and bondage and poverty for everyone else. Free enterprise creates 'a better distribution of all that has been produced so that more people enjoy more of our abundance than under any other system.' Unfortunately, many continue to promote the failed principles of socialism. Since the 1930s, laws have been passed to redistribute the income of American citizens through the federal tax system.[120] The Communist Manifesto written by Karl Marx and Friedrich Engels lists ten objectives of the communist party. The second objective is, 'A heavy progressive and graduated income tax,'[121] for the purpose of income redistribution on a grand scale. This clearly describes the current progressive and graduated federal tax system in the United States where income is taken from the top 60 percent of income earners, and given to the lowest 40 percent of income earner. [122]

"Aaron, you need to fight to remove the heavy progressive and graduated income tax which is a violation of the US Constitution and is, by definition, communism. These tax laws greatly restrict the freedom and prosperity of all citizens."

Thomas Jefferson interjected, "To create a nation that is free and prosperous requires 'a wise and frugal government . . . which shall leave [the citizens] . . . free to regulate their own pursuits of industry and improvement, and shall not take from the mouth of labor the bread it has earned.'[123] 'To take from one, because it is thought that his own industry and that of his fathers has acquired too much, in order to spare others, who, or whose fathers have not exercised equal industry and skill, is to violate arbitrarily the first principle of association, the guarantee to everyone of a free exercise of his industry and the fruits acquired by it.'[124]"

Franklin nodded at Jefferson in agreement and continued, "While 'a substantial part of the confiscation [and redistribution of wealth] is [done] by taxation, . . . the [socialists] were quick to recognize that if they wished to retain political power, the amount of taxation had to be limited and they had to resort to programs of massive deficit spending . . . to finance welfare expenditures on a large scale . . . The financial policy of the [socialists] requires that there be no way for the owners of wealth to protect themselves. This is the shabby secret of the [socialists] . . . Deficit spending is simply a scheme for the 'hidden' confiscation of wealth.'[125]

"As a result of the tax of deficit spending, the value of the American dollar declined in its purchasing power from one hundred cents in

1901 to approximately five cents in the year 2000. Over this hundred-year period, the government, through deficit spending, devalued the dollar 95 percent by inflation—in effect, a 95 percent tax. 'There is one, and only one, cause of inflation—expansion of the money supply faster than the growth of the nation's material assets. Whether those assets are gold and silver or food, machines and structures, the creation of money more rapidly than the creation of tangible items of value which people may want to purchase, floods the market place with more dollars than goods and dilutes the accepted value of money already in existence. In America, only the federal government can increase the money supply. Only government can create inflation. The most common method of increasing the money supply is spending more than is in the treasury and then merely printing extra money to make up the difference. Technically this is called deficit spending. Ethically, it is counterfeiting. Morally, it is wrong. Deficit spending, and the inflation it produces, constitutes a hidden tax against all Americans. Every time the dollar drops another penny in value, it is the same as if the government had counted up all the money that you and I had in our pockets, in savings, or investments, and then taxed us one cent on each dollar. The tax in this case, however, does not show up on our W-2 forms. It is hidden from view in the nature of higher and still higher prices for all that we buy.'[126]

"Aaron, you must fight to return to the principles of the original Constitution that have produced the greatest freedom and prosperity for the greatest number of people in the history of the world. Socialism also has a history—it has been a miserable failure each time attempted. Unfortunately, America has departed from many of the constitutional principles established by the founders. These departures have violated the Constitution and the rights of its citizens. They have added elements of socialism to the form of government we created.

"The restored Constitution will allow the general economy to operate on the basis of an honest, free-enterprise based competitive economy. Under the ideal system of Adam Smith's concept of free enterprise, the primary emphasis will be on freedom to choose. This means regulatory ordinances will be minimal. If the United States had retained the inspired formula of the original Constitution, the following would be true:

1. There would be no income taxes, no returns, and no audits.

2. There would be no withholding tax.

3. There would be no federal Social Security taxes.

4. Taxes would be as the Founders intended—based on an excise or sales tax.

5. There would be no national debt.

6. There would be no deficit spending.

7. The notorious Butler case of 1936 would never have been allowed. This is the decision of the Supreme Court, which unlawfully changed the 'general' welfare clause to include 'private' welfare. This opened the floodgates to socialism, profligate spending, and boosted the federal budget from $6 billion in 1936 to $600 billion by 1980, to over a $1 trillion by 1990 and $3.6 trillion in 2010.

8. There would be an honest money system based on gold and silver as the Constitution intended. All currency would be redeemable in gold or silver on demand.

9. The Federal Reserve would have been ruled unconstitutional. Even today, the Federal Reserve can be repealed by a majority of Congress under paragraph 31 of its charter and have all its assets turned over to the US Treasury as required by the original act.[127]

"Aaron, you must restore the principles of free enterprise found in the original Constitution; for free enterprise is the only economic system that recognizes our God-given rights of life, liberty, property, and the pursuit of happiness."

CHAPTER 14:
ABRAHAM LINCOLN

Franklin looked to Washington as if to turn the discussion back to him and then sat back in his chair. Washington rose to his feet and began, "Aaron, we have one final person to address you. As you will face issues and trials which divide the nation, there is no better man to instruct you. He 'died a martyr for his country, falling under the hand of a traitor assassin on the night of the 14th day of April 1865. The fourth anniversary of the beginning of the great War of Rebellion, through which he led the nation to a glorious triumph. . . The Great Republic loved him as its Father, and reverenced him as the preserver of its national life. The oppressed people of all lands looked up to him as the anointed of liberty, and hailed in him the consecrated leader of her cause. He struck the chains of slavery from four million . . . with a noble faith in humanity. . . By his wisdom, his prudence, his calm temper, his steadfast patience, his lofty courage, and his loftier faith, he saved the Republic from dissolution. By his simple integrity, he illustrated the neglected principles of its Constitution, and restored them to their just ascendancy. By all the results of his administration of its government, he inaugurated a New Era in the history of mankind. The wisdom of his statesmanship was excelled only by its virtuousness. Exercising a power which surpassed that of kings, he bore himself always as the servant of the people, and never its master.'[128]"

Washington sat in his seat, and Abraham Lincoln rose. "Aaron, I see today that many in your government are seeking socialized medicine in the United States." With a big smile on his face, Lincoln continued, "If this happens, where are all the people in Canada going to go to get good health care?" Everyone at the table laughed.

When the laughter subsided, Lincoln's countenance went solemn; he looked into Aaron's eyes, and said with conviction, "I support all you have been taught today. You have a great task ahead of you to restore the principles of the original Constitution. You have heard of the divinely appointed missions each at this table completed while on the earth. When I took the oath of office as the sixteenth President of the United States, 'I felt as though I were walking with destiny that my past life had been but a preparation for this hour for this trial . . . and I was sure I should not fail.'[129] Aaron, the life you have lived and this meeting today have prepared you to face the trials America is facing, and I am sure you will not fail.

"Many leaders of our country have forgotten that they are servants to the people. These leaders focus on their own power, prestige, and comforts at the expense of their children and grandchildren. Each set of politicians over the last several decades has left a larger burden of debt. Rather than face the challenges and sacrifice, they borrow tomorrow's money for their benefit today and leave the burden of repayment to future generations. This nation must stop borrowing from tomorrow.

"The prosperous have learned to resist the temptation to lose what matters most long-term for the short-term pleasure of something now. One of the biggest mistakes we make in life is that we give up what we want most for what we want right now. A tragic example of this tendency is found in the book of Genesis when Esau was hungry and sold his birthright to his brother Jacob for a bowl of stew. Do not let the American people sell their liberty and freedom for a bowl of government assistance. This nation must stop talking about handouts and entitlements and start talking about its duties and responsibilities.

"On multiple occasions I repaid debt and met financial obligations under severe distress. One of these incidences occurred in 1837, when I, and others, had incurred a large financial obligation. Many of those who owed the obligation were impoverished from the Panic of 1837 and were struggling financially. Some sought to be relieved of the burden by seeking a legislative amendment that would have removed the obligation, but I objected to such action saying, 'We have the benefit. Let us stand to our obligations like men.' These were trying times for each of us repaying the debt, and my financial condition was worse than penniless because of the burden of debt upon me. At times, I was unable to supply even my most pressing needs, but transferring the burden of this debt to another was not an option. I made great sacrifices to make each debt payment and finally, after eight long years, the debt was paid in full. The painfully liquidated note is now framed and displayed in a banking house in Springfield Illinois where all who enter may see. It serves as a memorial to the rectitude of the community during those trying times.[130] It is now time for each citizen of the United States to 'stand to their obligations like a man.' We need our citizens to say, 'What can I do today to make America better for tomorrow,' not, 'What can I borrow from tomorrow to make it better today.'

"Aaron, as you work to restore the Constitution and the greatness of America, you will be met with many challenges and failures. 'Always bear in mind that your own resolution to succeed is more important than any other.'[131]

"Christopher Columbus persisted for twenty years to find support for his sailing of the Atlantic, and persisted when all in his crew wanted to turn back. Columbus achieved a grand victory because he had the courage to press forward when all others had lost faith.

"George Washington and the Continental Army experienced many excruciating failures and defeats during the eight years of the Revolutionary War. The famous painter Charles Wilson Peale 'walked among these ragged troops of Washington's who had made the escape across from New Jersey and wrote about it in his diary. He said he'd never seen such miserable human beings in all his life—starving, exhausted, and filthy. One man in particular he thought was just the most wretched human being he had ever laid eyes on. He described how the man's hair was all matted and how it hung down over his shoulders. The man was naked except for what they called a blanket coat. His feet were wrapped in rags, his face all covered with sores from sickness. Peale was studying him when, all of a sudden, he realized that the man was his own brother.'[132] We should feel that all those who have fought and sacrificed for us are our brothers. We must remember what they went through, and yet they did not quit.

"There were many dark days during the Civil War with more than ten thousand military engagements, many of which were lost. Aaron, there will be thousands of battles in the effort to restore freedom, many of which may be lost, but you must persist toward the overall victory for liberty which will come. You must fight no matter how long and hard the road to freedom will be. God will strengthen and guide you, and your cause will not fail.

"You will be faced with tough choices. You must have the courage to be true to the oath you have taken to support and defend the US Constitution. You must be a hero of freedom and liberty and a champion to the millions of Americans who will come after you. You must leave America better than when you took office. You will be required to make sacrifices today for the benefit of those tomorrow.

"There were many that advised me against signing the Emancipation Proclamation, which eventually lead to the freedom of millions of slaves. As I was about to sign the document I was asked, 'Are you certain this is the right course of action?' I replied, 'I never, in my life have felt more certain that I was doing right, than I do in signing this paper.'[133]

"Booker T. Washington was born into slavery and recalled the day of emancipation that came when he was a boy. 'As the great day drew nearer, there was more singing in the slave quarters than usual. It was bolder, had more ring, and lasted later into the night. Most of the verses of the plantation songs had some reference to freedom. . . After the reading [of the Emancipation Proclamation] we were told that we were all free, and could go when and where we pleased. My mother, who was standing by my side, leaned over and kissed her children, while tears of joy ran down her cheeks. She explained to us what it all meant, that this was the day for which she had been so long praying, but fearing that she would never live to see. For some minutes there was great rejoicing and thanksgiving.'[134]

"On another occasion during the Civil War, a clergyman said to me, 'I hope the Lord is on our side.' I replied, 'I am not at all concerned about that for I know that the Lord is always on the side of the right. But it is my constant anxiety and prayer that this nation should be on the Lord's side.'[135] I worked diligently to do that which was right, to be on the Lord's side, without concern for power, position, and popularity. You must do the same. Aaron, there will be millions who will rejoice and give thanksgiving for the freedoms you will restore."

CHAPTER 15:
THE GIFT OF THE BLOODY SASH

Lincoln took his seat, and the room fell completely silent. During the discussion, Aaron had noticed a red sash sitting by Washington on the table and asked, "Mr. President, what is the red sash on the table?"

Washington answered, "The story of this sash goes back to the battle I shared at the beginning of our discussion. General Braddock came to America with two regiments of the British army to fight with the continental troops in the French and Indian war. He was seasoned in battle but was unfamiliar with the Indian mode of warfare. I was well acquainted with the Indian mode of warfare, so I warned General Braddock about the dangers of being ambushed and the need to have scouting parties. Prideful Braddock went into a rage and exclaimed, 'What! An American buskin teach a British general how to fight![136] These savages may indeed be a formidable enemy to your raw American militia, but upon the king's regular and disciplined troops,[137] they do not stand a chance.' The proud sixty-year-old general was not about to take advice from a twenty-three-year-old soldier.

"As we neared Fort Duquesne, I again approached the General and offered to take a team of scouts ahead to discover any awaiting ambushes. He again vehemently rejected the idea. General Braddock was so confident that his army would easily win the battle and take possession of Fort Duquesne that plans were made for a celebration with bonfires and fireworks.[138] The next day, disaster hit when we were ambushed. The General fought courageously but was wounded by a shot through the right arm and into his lung. Following the injury to General Braddock, I was able to form a rearguard, which allowed us to evacuate and disengage. I carried General Braddock to a cart, which then carried him from the battle.

"About a mile from the battle site our military surgeon, Dr. James Craik, treated the General's wounds. Braddock was very weak as he lay on the cart during our return march. On July 13, 1755, four days after battle, Braddock called me to his side and in a whisper said, 'Pride will cost me my life today.' He then took a decorative sash[139] from his uniform that was stained with blood saying, 'Please take this sash as a reminder of the cost of pride.' His eyes slowly closed, and he was gone. We buried our courageous General in the middle of the road and held a funeral service to honor him. We then rolled over the fresh ground to keep his grave from being found and desecrated by any Indians that might pursue."

Washington held up the sash so Aaron could see it clearly and said, "I carried this sash with me throughout my life as a reminder that I am to be a humble servant, acting as an instrument in the Hand of the

Almighty. I now give this sash to you, to act as a constant reminder to be a humble servant of the people."

Washington handed the sash to Aaron, and Aaron held the sash tightly. They each sat in silence as it become clear that the time of discussion had ended and the time for action was beginning. There was a feeling in the room that America was at a key point in its history—a point where freedom would be lost or restored depending on what happened in the days, months, and years ahead. Aaron felt the mantle of responsibility which had been placed on his shoulders, but he also felt the power and support from Almighty God and each of the men in the room. He knew his responsibilities were great, but he would never be alone.

CHAPTER 16:

AWAKING FROM THE COMA

As Aaron lay motionless in his hospital bed, his wife, Mary, held the hand of the husband she loved more than words could ever describe. She had stayed constantly by his side day and night for three days, holding his hand, praying that he would soon awaken. Even though her husband was in a coma, she wanted him to feel her love, devotion, and support.

Aaron came to a partial consciousness and realized someone was holding his hand tightly. It was a soft, feminine hand. It provided a warm, comforting reassurance that was hard to describe. As he looked to see whose hand it was, he saw his wife asleep at his side, her hand in his. The loving grip and sight of his wife gave him an enormous lift, and his eyes opened fully.

Aaron squeezed her hand tightly. "You're awake!" Mary could not hold back her joyous exclamation. "You're awake! You're awake!" she repeated as she embraced her husband. "I love you. I knew you would come back to me. I've missed you."

Aaron tightened his arms around his wife, basking in the comfort and joy that her presence always brought to him. "I love you, too," he told her as tears of joy ran down their cheeks. "Thank you for staying by my side. I pray I'll never face a day when you are not here. Of all the ways God has blessed me, giving you to me was the greatest. I cannot imagine life without you. Life with you is everything I always hoped it would be.[140]"

"How are you feeling?" Mary asked.

Rubbing the bump on his head he replied, "I feel good, but next time I think I'll try to land on my feet."

Mary laughed for the first time since the gunshots sounded. Their interaction was interrupted as two nurses and a doctor rushed into the room. Aaron was quickly surrounded by hospital staff checking his vitals. As one nurse grabbed his arm to take his blood pressure, Aaron jokingly said, "You better be careful or we'll both be in the tabloids in the morning." He then said to those around him, "I sure hope you're all patriots."

The doctors and nurses all laughed and the chief trauma surgeon, who was known to be a supporter of the socialist movement, replied, "Today, Mr. Vice President, we are all patriots."

All of Aaron's vitals were normal. The doctor said in amazement, "You're a very lucky man, Vice President Banner. You were shot multiple times, lay in a coma for three days, and yet somehow you're able to wake up in perfect health."

Aaron replied, "It is not luck. What you have witnessed is evidence of the miraculous hand of God protecting me. The Lord still has a work for me to do. 'I owe my life to God, and will try to serve him in every way I can.'[141]"

Aaron's countenance changed quickly to one of seriousness and solemnity. "I do appreciate the phenomenal care you have given me," Aaron began, "but I have a huge favor to ask. Mary will you please close the door? As Mary closed the hospital room door, Aaron asked, "Does anyone outside of this room know that I'm awake?"

"No," one of the nurses replied. The three of us were the only ones notified and we came directly to your room.

Aaron continued, "I need to ensure my recovery from this coma is not made public knowledge. It is essential for my personal safety, as well as for the security of this nation. There are evil people inside our government that are seeking to destroy our freedom who were behind this attempt on my life. Can you promise me you will do everything in your power to make sure my recovery is kept a secret until I meet with the President of the United States?"

Looks of shock lined the faces of each person in the room. Everyone nodded their heads in the affirmative. Aaron looked directly at his doctor and said, "I need to speak with the CEO of this hospital immediately, so we can organize a plan to ensure this secrecy. My life depends on it."

While waiting for the CEO to arrive, Mary told Aaron of the news that his chief of staff, Paula, had been rescued by an FBI agent after she crashed in the Potomac. A look of concern swept over Aaron's face. "Is she hurt?"

"No," Mary replied. "She's a little shaken up, but miraculously she was not injured."

"It seems that God has been watching over more than just me these last few days," Aaron said.

Aaron immediately turned to one of his staff members. "I need you to purchase several prepaid cell phones. Call Paula from one of these phones and ask her to buy several prepaid phones as well. Instruct Paula that once she has her phone and has found a secure location, to call the number you called her on.

Aaron turned to another staff member and said, "I need a disguise. Find me a wig, sunglasses, and a hat I can use."

The staff members left quickly to fulfill their assignments.

A few minutes later, there was a knock at the door. A secret service agent slowly opened the door to reveal Carl Watkins, the hospital's CEO. As Carl entered the room, the agent checked him for weapons.

"He's clean, sir," the agent said to Aaron.

"Thank you for meeting with me, Carl."

"Of course, Mr. Vice President. It's an honor for our hospital to have the opportunity to serve you."

Aaron proceeded to tell Carl about his need to keep his recovery a secret until after he had the opportunity to meet with President Daniels. "When will you be meeting with the President, sir?" Carl said.

"I'll most likely meet with him late this evening. My wife, Mary, will remain here so she's seen coming and going from my room. The few hospital staff who know of my recovery will be permitted to come in and out of the room, but the secret service agent at my room door will ensure that no one else comes in. I wanted to make sure you were aware of the situation so should any problems arise you can be sure to handle them. Can I count on you?"

"Absolutely, Mr. Vice President. We'll do everything in our power to ensure your recovery stays a secret."

"Thank you," Aaron replied as he extended his hand. The two shook hands, and the CEO departed.

Aaron turned to Mary and asked, "Do you think we can trust him?"

Mary nodded her head. "I believe so." He nodded as the door opened and an agent appeared.

He approached the bed and gave the Vice President the items he'd requested. Aaron handed one of the phones to Mary. "Will you please call Steve Clark and ask if I can use one of his jets today?" Steve was a good friend of the Banners who owned a very large corporation in the San Francisco area. He had several company jets his executives used for both business and pleasure.

Mary retrieved her personal cell phone to find his number and then began to dial on the prepaid phone. As she arranged for a jet, the prepaid cell phone the agent had used to call Paula began to ring.

Aaron picked up the phone and answered it but remained silent. After a couple seconds of silence, Paula's voice came through the receiver, "Hello, Hello?"

"Paula, it is good to hear your voice. I'm so glad you're okay," said Aaron.

"It is great to hear your voice as well, sir. Are you okay?"

"I'm in perfect health, "Aaron replied. "I'll explain more about that later. Right now I need you to fill me in on what has happened during the last few days."

Paula related the flurry of events that transpired in her life since the assassination attempt: the recovery of the envelopes, the fall into the Potomac River, the rescue by Agent Johnson, and the fire in her office. She shared with Aaron that she felt confident that Agent Johnson was working with the enemy, and how she had tricked him into believing that all of the information she'd received from the Vice President had been destroyed.

Finally, she told Aaron that she'd been able to successfully deliver the one remaining package safely into the hands of Charles Morrell. As she concluded her synopsis Paula lamented, "I'm so sorry I lost some of the information."

"You did a great job, Paula," Aaron reassured her. "I'm relieved that you're safe. Thank you for your heroic efforts. We will be able to fill in many of the missing pieces. I've been working to secure indisputable evidence regarding the ultimate leaders of these crimes against our country. I wanted to be certain of my accusations before I turned anything over to the proper authorities. I'm only sorry that I didn't find those final pieces before all this happened. Honestly, I was hoping you would not have to get involved, but it looks like you were more than capable of handling the challenge. Will you please have Charles call me from a secure, unmonitored line at this number?"

"I will," Paula replied.

Aaron concluded his call with Paula and turned to Mary, who had finished her phone conversation a few minutes prior. "Steve said the jet is at your disposal. It'll be ready in an hour."

Aaron asked Mary for his clothes and began to get dressed. He put on the wig, hat, and glasses, and asked her, "How do I look?"

Mary answered with a chuckle, "You look just fine. You definitely don't look like Vice President Banner."

Aaron began putting his personal items into his pockets, and as he reached his hand into his right pocket, he found that it was already full. He pulled out the red sash he'd received in heaven. He froze for a moment, mesmerized by the item he held in his hand.

Mary saw the sash and asked, "What's that?"

"It is a gift from George Washington." Aaron replied.

Mary thought her husband must be joking, but she didn't get the joke. "What are you talking about, sweetheart?"

"This is a gift of great significance, Mary. It will be a national treasure. It's a symbol of the hand of God in the freedom of America and the importance of being a nation under God that lives by its motto, 'In God We Trust.'"

Mary again asked, "So what is it?" Before he could explain further, Aaron's cell phone began to ring. He answered the phone to hear an agent inform him his car had arrived.

"Mary, my car's ready. I promise to explain everything later. The story behind this sash will be told many, many times. I love you, and I'll see you very soon."

Aaron gave his wife a kiss and headed for the door.

CHAPTER 17:
RETURN TO WASHINGTON, DC

With the help of the hospital staff and his agents, Aaron made his way from the room to the car without arousing any suspicion. As they began driving toward the private runway, Aaron's cell phone rang.

Aaron answered with a simple, "Hello."

The voice on the other end replied, "Vice President Banner, this is Charles Morrell. How are you feeling?"

"I'm in great physical condition, Charles, which is a good thing, because we have a lot of work ahead of us. Have you been able to secure the information?"

"I have made multiple copies and hidden them in various locations, sir."

"Good. I was able to sneak out of the hospital, and I'm on my way to Washington, DC now. My wife and others are still at the hospital to secure the cover that I'm still in a coma. I need you to bring a copy of the materials with you to the White House this evening. We are going to meet with President Daniels."

"Do you really think it's a good idea to meet with the President, sir? The evidence shows he had some involvement in the crimes and cover-up. They've already tried to kill you once. What's stopping them from trying to kill you again, and me along with you? The President is the most powerful man in the world."

To begin with, Charles, President Daniels is not the most powerful man in the world or even in America. God is. Secondly, I have been friends with President Daniels for two decades now. While the evidence is clear that he had knowledge and involvement in crimes and cover-ups, I don't believe he knew the full extent of the corruption or that he ordered to have me assassinated. While this is a possibility, my gut is telling me he is the best person to help us. How long will it take you to get to the White House?"

"I can get there in thirty minutes."

"Great. I'll call you when I'm closer so we can plan to arrive at the White House at the same time."

"Will the President know we're coming, sir?"

"No. I think it'll be safest to keep the cover of my coma intact until we're in the White House later this evening. Obviously, once I enter, the cat will be out of the bag. It will be a surprise visit, but given my relationship with the President and the events of the past few days, I'm confident that President Daniels will meet with me despite the lack of notice."

"Sounds good to me, sir. I'll be waiting for your call."

Charles hung up the phone, amazed he was going to have a late night rendezvous with the President about his involvement in criminal activity. He went to work preparing a copy of the information to give to Vice President Banner. He printed several files he thought would be more effective in printed form than on a computer screen.

Aaron sat in the car thinking about the enormous changes that would occur in the hours, days, and months ahead. He had so many calls he wanted to make but knew he could not take the risk of blowing his cover. Instead, he sat back and began writing down his experience in heaven and the stories and principles he had been taught.

He arrived at the private runway without incident. Aaron was pleased to see the plane that Mary had arranged for him was a Cessna Citation Ten, one of the world's fastest business jets, powered by two Rolls-Royce engines. Aaron had obtained his pilot license two decades earlier and enjoyed flying when he could. He had arranged to fly the plane himself to minimize the number of people aware of his travel.

He had even left his security detail at the hospital, feeling he was safer if he was the only one who knew when or where he was landing. He performed the necessary safety checks, got into the jet, took the pilot's seat, and readied for takeoff. With a cruising speed of six hundred miles per hour, he estimated his travel time to Washington, DC to be around three and a half hours.

It had been a long time since he had flown by himself, and he looked forwarded to flying one of the world's finest business jets. The flight went smoothly with minimal turbulence. Mary arranged for him to land at a private runway outside of Washington, DC owned by their friend, Harry McCormic. The sun had set, and the sky was dark. As he was approaching his destination, he could see the lighted runway below, and prepared to land.

Aaron brought the plane to a stop on the runway. As he exited the plane, Harry was there to greet him. "Welcome home, Aaron. How was the flight?"

"Wonderful. It felt great to be in the cockpit of such an impressive aircraft and to have some time to myself."

"I concur with you on that, Aaron. It certainly is an impressive aircraft. I'll take the jet into the hanger and handle everything from here. The car you requested is parked over there. It has a full tank of gas, and the keys are in the ignition. Is there anything else I can do?"

Aaron gave Harry a slap on the back. "No, but thank you for all your help. When I return the car, we'll have to catch up a bit. I'd like to hear about your recent trip to Italy."

"Sure thing," Harry answered.

Aaron headed toward the car, and as he walked, he pulled out his cell phone to call Charles.

"Charles, it's Aaron. I'm getting into a car right now to drive to the White House; I'll meet you at the entrance to the Eisenhower Executive Office Building in thirty minutes. We should draw less attention entering the office building. We can then enter the White House through the tunnel. We'll contact the President once we're in the White House."

"Yes, sir. I have everything ready for the meeting. I'll see you in thirty minutes."

CHAPTER 18:

MEETING AT THE WHITE HOUSE

Charles pulled into the parking lot of the Eisenhower Building and looked towards the designated meeting point but did not see Vice President Banner. He parked and walked to the entrance and waited, his heart racing. Within a few minutes a sedan with tinted windows pulled into the parking lot. "Well," Charles thought, "it's either the Vice President or someone here to kill me. I sure hope it's the Vice President."

He waited anxiously for the car to park and for the driver to exit the vehicle. He breathed a sigh of relief as he saw Vice President Banner emerge.

Aaron walked briskly to the entrance of the building and extended his hand to Charles. "Thank you for meeting me here, Charles. I know that you have put your life at risk by coming tonight. Your acts of bravery and valor will bless this country for years to come. Thank you."

"It's an honor to serve both you and this great nation, Mr. Vice

President." Charles held up a folder filled with papers and said, "Here is the information you requested. I have some of the information printed here." Reaching into one of his pockets he continued, "There are three copies . . ."

Without warning, the deafening sound of gunfire emerged, brutally interrupting Charles's words. The screeching of tires accompanied the loud shots, and a dark SUV careened down the street, swerving to reenter traffic. Aaron found himself on the ground with a throbbing pain in his chest. He said a silent prayer of thanks that his security detail had insisted he put on a bulletproof vest before he left the hospital.

Aaron gingerly pulled himself to a sitting position and turned toward where Charles lay on the pavement. "Charles! Charles!"

There was no response. Aaron could see blood pooling under Charles's head. He reached out to check for a pulse and found nothing. Aaron sat for a very brief moment, stunned. He quickly swept his hand through Charles's coat pocket, finding the promised jump drives nestled in its depths. He hastily grabbed the folder and tried to stand but immediately fell to one knee. Sharp pains radiated through his chest. He quickly rubbed his hand over his chest and checked for blood but found none.

Aaron took a deep breath and attempted to stand again, this time with success. He raced through the entrance of the building where multiple members of security, responding to the gunshots, met him. He quickly related what happened and insisted he be taken immediately to the Presidential Emergency Operations Center, or the PEOC.

One secret service agent stayed to tend to Charles, and two agents escorted the Vice President to the bunker. As they made their way, the lead agent said, "Mr. Vice President. I thought you were in a coma in California."

"I was," Aaron answered simply as they entered the tunnel. He continued, "It seems there are some people that want to put me in a permanent one."

When they arrived at the White House, they opened a door revealing a hidden stairwell and began the descent down the numerous flights that led to the bunker a hundred feet beneath the east wing. The bunker was built during WWII for President Franklin D. Roosevelt. They came to the end of the stairs and exited into a tunnel that led to the PEOC bunker.

The agents wasted no time getting Vice President Banner into the safety of this sanctuary and closed the door behind them.

"I'm going to call for a meeting with the President," Aaron informed the agents. "Please make sure that he is the only one allowed into this room." When he was assured that his order would be carried out, he asked the agents to leave the bunker and secured the door behind him.

As Aaron sat in isolated silence, he tried to focus his mind on his impending meeting with President Daniels—a meeting he dreaded more with each passing moment. He was still breathing heavily from the hurried pace to the PEOC, so he sat for a moment to catch his breath and collect his thoughts. Aaron set the blood-spattered folder down on a table, reached for the phone, and dialed the President's extension.

After several minutes of waiting, a familiar voice came on the line. "Aaron, are you there?"

"Yes, Walt. I'm here. We need to talk."

"I just heard about the shooting outside of the Office Building. Are you okay?" The concern in President Daniels voice sounded sincere.

"I will have a couple of serious bruises and maybe a broken rib, but I'm fine. Charles Morrell was not as lucky. He was killed right in front of me. We need to talk, Walt. Will you meet with me right now in the PEOC?"

"I'm on my way now, Aaron"

"Thank you, Walt. And please, keep this meeting a secret. It's better if no one knows we are meeting."

"Of course," replied President Daniels. "I'll see you soon."

Aaron hung up the phone and turned his attention to the evidence. He opened the folder Charles Morrell had assembled and reviewed the information, highlighting the items to address with President Daniels. Aaron was still unsure how to proceed. He had a desire to punch President Daniels in the face, wrestle him to the ground, and demand an answer as to why he betrayed his country and their friendship of twenty years. Although the thought was tempting, Aaron knew this approach would be ineffective. If he was to have any hope of holding those involved responsible, he must present the information he had and then listen to the President's explanation.

The door to the bunker swung open and President Daniels entered. He was still dressed in his suit pants and white shirt but had removed his tie and jacket. President Daniels walked toward Aaron and extended his hand. Aaron could not bring himself to take it and stayed in his chair.

"Have a seat, Walt," he said, his tone cold.

President Daniels stopped his advance and sat down in a chair next to Aaron. "You seem very angry with me, Aaron. What's wrong?"

Aaron could feel his blood pressure rising. "What's wrong? I'll tell you what's wrong." His voice rose with every word. "You tried to have me killed, that's what's wrong. Not once, but twice, and I had to watch a good man die to cover up your crimes!" Aaron was on his feet, his fists clenched, his face red. "You betrayed both me and your county, and you have the audacity to sit there, look me in the eyes, and ask 'What's wrong?'"

His idea to keep his cool and listen to the President obviously had not gone as planned. Aaron threw the blood-covered folder onto the table in front of the President and said, "Here's the proof." The force with which Aaron threw the folder caused a few of the papers to scatter across the floor.

President Daniels bent down to pick up the papers and scanned the documents. He then opened the folder and thumbed through the pages. As he looked through the information, President Daniels lowered his head and began to cry, "I'm sorry Aaron," he said, his voice choked with remorse. "I never thought anyone would get hurt."

This was not the response Aaron expected, and they both sat in silence for a few moments. President Daniels softly quoted a passage from *The Screwtape Letters*, a book they both had read several times. "The safest road to Hell is a gradual one—the gentle slope, soft underfoot, without sudden turnings, without milestones, without signposts."[142]

"I can't believe I let myself get pulled into this," President Daniels said as he held up the folder, "but I was unaware of the majority of this information. I know that you have little reason to trust me,

Aaron, but I hope you will try. Please tell me what you know."

Aaron could feel the President's sincerity and remorse. He replied, "Just over a week ago, Senator Mark Thompson contacted me for assistance in exposing and bringing to justice evil alliances within the government that involved bribery, prostitution, treason, secret murders, and other crimes.

"Mark was approached to join this group several years ago and was shocked by their offer. By joining this alliance, he would vote as they directed and assist them when needed. In exchange, they would ensure his elections and increase his power, control, and wealth. His immediate reaction was to reject them boldly and organize an investigation. Mark realized this approach would have little impact on this evil organization. In order to really stop the group and bring the leaders to justice, he would have to do it from the inside. He joined the alliance and began collecting information on their secret evil works and their relationships both inside and outside of the government. Mark gave me a copy of the information he had collected over the years and felt he had enough information and knowledge on some of the leaders involved to fully expose their corruption and to bring it to an end."

President Daniels suddenly interjected, "Did you know that Mark was killed in a plane crash shortly after you were shot at Stanford?"

Aaron felt his body sway, the shock of another death hitting him hard. He took several deep breaths and while shaking his bowed head said, "Somehow this group must have learned of the information Mark collected and of his contact with me. I am confident that research into the crash will reveal sabotage and murder. These people are ruthless, willing to do whatever it takes to keep their organization a secret and preserve their positions of power, status, and wealth."

Aaron raised his head and looked at President Walter Daniels. "How could you do it, Walt? Why did you assist this group, and what was your level of involvement?"

President Daniels stared down at the papers spread across the table. "During the election, I was approached with information regarding an affair in my past. I was told this information would be made public unless I agreed to pardon a certain individual if I was elected President. I knew that if the information about my affair were made public it would destroy any chance of winning the election. I did research into the individual they requested the pardon for, and it did not seem to be of great significance.

"Almost every President before me had pardoned individuals with crimes that far exceeded the crimes of the requested pardon, so I agreed. I rationalized that this was a small concession in exchange for all the good I could do as President. Throughout my presidency, they've asked for small favors here and there and have provided me with occasional favors in return. You have to believe me, Aaron. I was unaware of the extent of these crimes that you have laid before me tonight. None of the items they requested of me seemed to be of great significance, and I rationalized it as politics. A necessary evil to get the things I wanted to accomplish done."

The President sat back in his chair and brought his hands over his eyes, rubbing his forehead. "It seems as if I have fallen as King David did. In my attempt to cover my sin of adultery, I have assisted in the committing of murder. I have done great wrongs. I have betrayed your trust and friendship. If I'm to get through this, Aaron,

I need your friendship and support. Can you forgive me?"

Aaron felt that Walt's remorse, guilt, and sorrow were sincere. He rose to his feet and approached President Daniels's chair. Walt rose to his feet, and Aaron wrapped his arms around him, giving the President a tremendous hug. "I love you, Walt. You will always be my friend and brother. Yes, I forgive you. We'll get through this."

The President, overcome with emotion, said nothing during the embrace, but tears poured down his face.

As they were returning to their seats, Aaron asked, "So Mr. President, what do you recommend we do next?"

President Daniels sat up in his chair and, with conviction, replied, "It is time for me to end the lies. Tomorrow I will speak to the American people and tell them what I have told you. I will then announce my resignation. You will be sworn in as the new President of the United States. If you will permit me, Aaron, I would like to assist you in bringing those involved with these evil alliances to justice."

Aaron replied, "We shall see. Looks like we both have a lot of preparations to make and speeches to write for tomorrow. I will be praying for you, my friend. I think it safest for me to stay here in the PEOC this evening."

President Daniels nodded his head in agreement and left the PEOC to return to the White House residence. He knew he would soon be having a very difficult discussion with his wife, followed by painful discussions with his children and staff in the morning.

As Aaron was again alone in the bunker, a flood of thoughts poured into his mind. He wrote down the ideas—one of which was the security of his family. Aaron began arranging for his family's increased security and began coordinating their trip to the White House.

CHAPTER 19:

RESIGNATION

President Daniels sat in the chair behind the desk in the oval office for the last time. He glanced over his notes as final preparations were made around him. As he gazed up, he saw his beautiful wife, Patricia, talking with Aaron and Mary Banner. His discussion with his wife the evening before had been profoundly difficult, and he hoped and prayed his mistakes would not cost him what he held most dear: his family. He recognized it would be hard to rebuild the trust and relationships he had damaged. Patricia looked in his direction and their eyes met. He gave her a smile. She smiled back at him, giving him hope that their relationship could be mended.

The countdown to the live broadcast began. He shifted his gaze to the camera in front of him and took a deep breath. The light indicating live transmission turned on, and President Daniels began, "I address you today from the Oval Office of the White House in response to the horrific events that have transpired over the past few days. As you know, there was an assassination attempt on Vice President Banner while he addressed Stanford University four days ago. He was in a coma for several days. The Vice President's assassination attempt was not the only devastating event on that day. Senator Mark Thompson was killed in a plane crash shortly after the attempt on Vice President Banner's life. Later that day, Vice President Banner's chief of staff, Paula Brackett, was forced off the road into the Potomac River. Thankfully, Paula survived the accident, sustaining only minor injuries. Yesterday, Vice President Banner awoke from his coma and returned to Washington. Shortly after arriving, he was shot in the chest outside of the Eisenhower Executive Office Building in another attempted assassination. Gratefully, Vice President Banner was wearing a bulletproof vest, which stopped two bullets. Unfortunately, the man accompanying the Vice President, Charles Morrell, a man who has served this country for decades, was not as fortunate. He was killed instantly."

"I am going to speak to you plainly and boldly about the evil alliances behind these criminal acts. There will be no cover story or cover up. The message I bring to you today is not a happy one, but it is the truth. Some of my closest advisors suggested that I cannot tell the American people what really happened, that it would be too dangerous and disruptive to the country. I disagree. The American people deserve the truth. The Bible declares, 'You shall know the truth and the truth shall set you free.'[143]

"Americans need to know that groups can and have engaged in plots to destroy our freedoms and are engaged in acts of deceit and murder for power, fame, wealth, and their own nefarious socialist goals. These secret works of darkness in our past and very recent history must be brought to light if they are to be destroyed in the present and prevented in the future. Those who do not learn from history are condemned to repeat it. If we are to restore and preserve the principles of freedom America was founded upon, these evil alliances must be done away with.

"A strategy that both these evil alliances and the devil use to keep their evil works secret is to say that such organizations and groups do not exist, and they discount anyone that raises such concerns as crazy conspiracy theorists. There is no conspiracy theory, but there is conspiracy fact. These evil alliances have existed since the beginning of time when Cain murdered his brother that his flocks might fall into his hands. The Bible records that Cain entered into a secret covenant with Satan to kill his brother and then declared, 'Truly I am . . . the master of this great secret, that I may murder and get gain.'[144]

"There are numerous examples throughout history of these evil groups and the destruction and evil they have promulgated. 'We must realize that there have been Hitlers and Lenins and Stalins and Caesars and Alexander the Greats throughout history. Why should we assume there are no such men today with perverted lusts for power?'[145]

"I have heard some say that yes, there are numerous examples throughout history of evil alliances and conspiracies, but such groups do not exist in America. History teaches us otherwise. Two American Presidents, Abraham Lincoln and John F. Kennedy, were killed by evil conspiracies. The assassinations and cover-ups included members of their own government. I declare that these evil alliances and conspiracies continue today and are more highly organized, more cleverly disguised, and more powerfully promoted than ever before in their lust for power, wealth, and control of America and the entire world.

"I met with Vice President Banner last night after the second attempt on his life. He brought to my attention proof that each of these attacks of the past four days were orchestrated by individuals within our government and other positions of power, to keep their secret evil alliances and crimes from being revealed. Senator Mark Thompson obtained much information about those involved, their structure, goals, and crimes, which he shared with Vice President Banner. Those implicated by this information have been working to destroy the evidence against them. Our nation is under attack by an enemy from within.

"I am very sad to report to you that even I was drawn into the corruption of this group, to cover up an extramarital affair. While I had no knowledge of the extensive corruption, fraud, and murders these alliances were involved in, I did provide favors to members of this evil group. My actions were easy to rationalize as the game of 'politics' and 'small evils' with no victims, necessary to get the things I wanted to accomplish done. It is now very clear how mistaken I was.

"I have done great wrong. I have betrayed the marriage covenants I made to my wife. I have betrayed this country and the oath of office I have taken. As I met with Vice President Banner last night, it became clear the serious mistakes I have made and the consequences of those mistakes. I am filled with enormous pain, anguish, and sorrow. I ask for your forgiveness. I will work for the remainder of my life to restore the trust of each who had looked to me as a leader and an example. I will work each day to repair my relationships with my wife, my children, my colleagues, and with the American people. I will work to heal the wounds and damage I have caused."

The President paused as his eyes filled with tears, his voice cracking, "I am so sorry. I am so sorry."

The President gained his composure and continued, "I will also work to bring those involved to justice for the murder of both Charles Morrell and Mark Thompson, and to rid our land of these workers of darkness. I am now resigning as President of the United States. It has been an honor to serve this great country and people. Immediately following the conclusion of my remarks, Vice President Banner will be sworn in as the new President of the United States and address the nation. Vice President Banner is a man of integrity and honor. He is a man this country can proudly call their President. His ability as a leader is excelled only by his virtue and character. I will pray each day for our new President, and I ask that each of you do the same. My final words to you as your President come from the mouth of the true leader of this nation recorded in the Bible, "If my people who are called by my name will humble themselves and pray and seek my face and turn from their wicked ways, then I [The Lord] will hear from heaven, and I will forgive their sin and heal their land.'[146]"

Walter felt relief and sadness as he ended his remarks. He knew that the days ahead would be very difficult, but he also knew that he would not be alone. His loving wife, Patricia, and his best friend, Aaron, were still at his side. Whatever came, he knew that with their help, and the help of the Lord, he would recover.

CHAPTER 20:
THE NEW PRESIDENT

The camera continued to roll as former President Daniels rose from his chair and exited the screen. The cameras then turned to Vice President Banner, standing with Chief Justice John Burger in the Oval Office as he prepared to take the oath of office. Chief Justice Burger began saying, "Mr. Vice President, are you prepared to take the oath of office as President of the United States of America?"

Vice President Banner replied, "Yes, I am."

Chief Justice Burger continued, "At your request, I hold in my hand the Bible that George Washington placed his hand on when he took the oath as the first President of the United States. Please place your left hand on the Bible, and raise your right arm to the square and repeat after me.

"I, Aaron Washington Banner, do solemnly swear that I will faithfully execute the office of President of the United States and will, to the best of my ability, preserve, protect, and defend the Constitution of the United States."

Following the example set by George Washington, President Banner repeated the oath, took the Bible is his hand, and reverently kissed it. He looked heavenward and said, "So help me God."[147]

The camera followed President Banner as he walked to and took his seat at the Presidential desk in the Oval Office to address the nation as their new servant. President Banner looked into the camera and began, "As I have reflected on these past four dark days in American history, as evil powers and alliances have murdered and attempted to murder American patriots to further their power, wealth, and control, my mind was taken to the life of Winston Churchill and his battle with the evil Nazi alliances. Churchill became Prime Minister of England on May 10, 1940 at a 'time when the powerful German air force was making round-the-clock trips . . . dumping planeload after planeload of bombs on England. No one knew whether the British would be able to hold out for another week or a month.'[148]

"'The outlook was bleak. The Nazis were running over France, Belgium, and Holland. Joseph P. Kennedy, the American ambassador in London, told Washington that Britain was finished.'[149] In the mists of the gloom and turmoil and in the face of what seemed to others like impossible odds, Churchill took office with optimism and determination. Churchill wrote of the day he took office, 'I felt as though I were walking with destiny that my past life had been but a preparation for this hour for this trial . . . and I was sure I should not fail.'[150]

"On May 13, 1940, Churchill gave his first speech as Prime

Minister to the House of Commons. He said, 'You ask, what is our aim? I can answer in one word: victory . . . victory in spite of all the terror, victory however long and hard the road may be . . . with all the strength that God can give us . . . I take up my task with buoyancy and hope, I feel sure that our cause will not be suffered to fail.'[151]

"Even during the worst of times, Churchill remained optimistic and confident that they would achieve victory. During a BBC broadcast, Churchill proclaimed: 'We are resolved to destroy Hitler and every vestige of the Nazi regime. From this, nothing will turn us—nothing. We will never parley, we will never negotiate with Hitler or any of his gang. We shall fight him by land, we shall fight him by sea, we shall fight him in the air, until, with God's help, we have rid the earth of his shadow.'[152]

"After five hard years of battle, victory was achieved. On May 8, 1945, via broadcast, Churchill announced that Germany had signed the act of unconditional surrender. Churchill declared, 'The German war is therefore at an end. . . From this Island and from our united Empire, [we] maintained the struggle single-handed for a whole year until we were joined by the military might of Soviet Russia, and . . . the United States of America. . . Finally almost the whole world was combined against the evil-doers, who are now prostrate before us. . . We must now devote all our strength and resources to the completion of our task, both at home and abroad. . . Long live the cause of freedom! . . . [We should now] give humble and reverent thanks to Almighty God for our deliverance from the threat of German domination.'[153]

"'Churchill's actions were pivotal in one of the great and most dramatic turning points of civilization. . . He knew that if he could rally the mind, spirit, and heart of the British people, they would eventually emerge victorious. . . Churchill not only saved Britain from defeat but now in retrospect, he saved democracy as a form of government in the world. Here was truly a single individual whose life made a profound difference to everyone on our planet.'[154]

"Today our nation is under attack by evil forces who seek to destroy the inspired principles of freedom in the United States Constitution. I have just taken an oath to preserve, protect and defend the Constitution of the United States. I would now ask each of you to take the same oath and join me in the battle against evil to preserve, protect, and defend the Constitution of the United States and restore the freedoms that so many before us fought and sacrificed for.

"We are at a critical point in the history of this nation which is on the brink of bondage. We are now faced with the choice that the Founders of this nation faced when George Washington declared, 'We must now determine to be enslaved or free. If we make freedom our choice, we must obtain it by the blessing of Heaven on our united and vigorous efforts.'[155] The great men and women of this nation must again unite to work and fight for freedom as did our inspired founders. In a speech delivered to some who thought it better to have peace and bondage than fight for freedom, Patrick Henry said, 'If we wish to be free . . . we must fight! . . . Is life so dear, or peace so sweet, as to be purchased at the price of chains and slavery? Forbid it, Almighty God! I know not what course others may take; but as for me, give me liberty or give me death!'[156] If our children and grandchildren are to be free, we must fight. We must not sit idly by as evil people and organizations infiltrate our country and government. 'He who passively accepts evil is as much involved in it as he who helps to perpetrate it. He who accepts evil without protesting against it is really cooperating with it.'[157]

"It took a revolutionary war to obtain our freedom from England, it took a war to destroy the evil of Nazism, and it will take a war to reclaim our country's freedom. However, it will not be a war with guns, but a war of votes, words, education, and the unity and vigorous effort of each American to support, defend, and live the principles of freedom found in the inspired Constitution. 'None of those noble words about life, liberty, and the pursuit of happiness, about all men being created equal—none of that would have been worth any more than the paper it was written on had it not been for those who were fighting to make it happen.'[158] America needs modern patriots to fight against the unconstitutional and tyrannical efforts of many in our government and society. The God of heaven sent some of the wisest, noblest, and bravest men and women to lay the foundation of a free America, and God has again sent many wise, noble, and brave men and women to preserve and restore it.

"With the information obtained from the late Senator Mark Thompson, we will begin working to bring to justice each person involved with these secret works of darkness and in these evil alliances. We will bring their crimes and socialist agendas to an end. Yes, the battle will be long. Yes, the battle will be hard. And yes, there will be pain and sacrifice, but with the help and guidance of the Almighty God, we will succeed. Victory will be ours, and their wickedness will be destroyed. God wants us to be free.

"It is time for us as a nation to end the reign of corrupt and socialistic politicians and elect to office men and women of character who love freedom and desire to serve God and their fellow man. We need to elect men and women who will live and honor the oath of office to support and defend the Constitution. John Adams wrote, 'Because power corrupts, society's demands for moral authority and character increase as the importance of the position increases.'[159] We must not be lead astray by the lie that indiscretions in private life will not affect service in public life. The Bible declares, 'Whoever is faithful in small matters will be faithful in large ones [and] whoever is dishonest in small matters will be dishonest in large ones.'[160]

"We need to elect more men and women like George Washington. Washington was not chosen as general of the Continental Army because he was a powerful speaker or 'because he was a great military leader. . . . Washington had never commanded an army in battle before. . . He was chosen because they knew him; they knew the kind of man he was; they knew his character, his integrity.'[161] Abigail Adams, wife of John Adams, wrote of Washington, 'No man ever lived, more deservedly beloved and respected. . . [he] maintained a modest diffidence of his own talents . . . Possesst of power, possesst of an extensive influence, he never used it but for the benefit of his Country.'[162] Washington recognized he was merely an instrument in the hands of God. In a speech following victory in the Revolutionary War, he stated, 'I attribute all the glory to a Supreme Being . . . who was able by the humblest instruments . . . to establish and secure the liberty and happiness of these United States.'[163]

"At his death, Congressman Henry Lee said of Washington, 'First in war, first in peace, and first in the hearts of his countrymen . . . Correct throughout, vice shuddered in his presence and virtue always felt his fostering hand; the purity of his private character gave effulgence to his public virtues... Such was the man for whom our nation mourns.'[164]

"Washington was a patriot whose soul did joy in the liberty and freedom of his country. He was a man more concerned with deeds than words, who fought and labored intensely for his people. Through his firm faith in Christ and selfless devotion to country, he lived his motto, 'For God and my Country.'[165]

"After victory in the Revolutionary War, there were desires by some to make George Washington king. The first Congress voted to pay Washington a salary of twenty-five thousand dollars a year (approximately five hundred thousand in today's dollars). Washington, however, chose to continue his work as an unpaid servant of the people. During his years as commander in chief of the Continental Army, he took no pay. He would do the same during his eight years as the first President of the United States. George Washington said in his inaugural address of 1789, "When I was first honored with a call into the service of my country, then on the eve of an arduous struggle for its liberties, the light in which I contemplated my duty required that I should renounce ... compensation. From this resolution I have in no instance departed. And being still under the impressions which produced it, I must decline [compensation]." He exemplified the word of the Savior, 'But he that is greatest among you shall be your servant.'[166]

"Today I am honored to accept the call into the service of my country as the fifty-first President of the United States. It is an honor and a privilege to serve this great nation, and I will accept no pay as I fulfill my duties and service as President. I will also work diligently to reduce and limit the expenditures of the executive office.

"As I have studied the lives of those who sacrificed and toiled to establish this great nation, I am filled with great gratitude and inspired by their love of freedom and willingness to serve and sacrifice for the benefit of those who would follow them. Many surrendered their lives as a portion of the price paid for the liberties we enjoy. Their willing spirits never murmured or regretted the sacrifices required to obtain freedom. Instead, they considered it an honor and privilege to be a part of the fight for the great cause of freedom. Our founding fathers were willing to risk their lives, fortunes, and sacred honor to establish freedom, while many of our current political leaders are willing to risk our freedom for their power, fame, and wealth.

"We, the blessed recipients of freedom, must not let this happen. It is our duty to cherish, preserve, protect, and defend the inheritance they have left each of us. This nation needs each of you to fight against evil, oppression, and corruption and replace it with goodness, freedom, and honor. There were many patriots and heroes during the founding of America, and in the days, months, and years ahead, there will be many modern patriots and heroes whom the Lord will raise up, direct, and protect to restore the freedoms of America.

"As you are aware, four days ago, members of evil alliances and their minions attempted to have me assassinated by snipers at the Stanford University Commencement. I was shot multiple times, from several directions, and I was not wearing any protective gear. When I awoke from my coma yesterday, I found myself in perfect health. Some may view this as luck, but I know it was not luck. I know my safety was the result of the miraculous hand of God protecting me."

President Banner held up a dress shirt and continued, "I have with me the shirt that I was wearing during the commencement speech. In it you will find five bullet holes. Although five bullets pierced my shirt, not one pierced my body. I am having this shirt put on display at the White House Visitor Center as a reminder that God is the leader of this country, and that we are guided and protected by His hand. This Divine miracle should awaken inside of each American a remembrance that we indeed are 'One Nation, Under God' whose motto is 'In God We Trust.'

"As a nation we have strayed from some of the divine laws and principles of our Supreme Creator. We must recognize God's hand in our life and the great need we have as a nation for His protection and guidance. As a Nation we need to heighten our devotion, trust, and gratitude towards God who is the true founder and leader of this country. There are those who are fighting to remove God and prayer from our nation. They claim they are doing so in the name of tolerance, freedom, and open-mindedness, but the truth is that they are intolerant of religion because it interferes with their socialist agendas. 'Religion needs defenders against those who care only for the interest of the state. I believe that faith and religion play a critical role in the political life of our nation . . . Without God, democracy will not and cannot long endure. If we ever forget that we are one nation under God, then we will be a nation gone under.'[167]

"I know that you have not elected me with your votes, but I would ask that you sustain me with your prayers.[168] We are not alone in our battle. As we pray, we will have the support and assistance of God and His angels. The Bible declares, 'Though a host encamp against me, my heart shall not fear; though war arise against me, yet I will be confident . . . Be strong in the Lord and in the power of His might.'[169]

"George Washington and the early patriots often observed a day of fasting and prayer to give thanks to God and to pray for His guidance and support. I propose that this Sunday, as a nation, we have a day of fasting and prayer to give thanks to God and pray for His guidance and support. I do appreciate your prayers for me and know that I will be praying daily for you and for our country that we will have the blessing and guidance of heaven in fulfilling the oath we have taken today to preserve, protect, and defend the inspired Constitution of the United States."

President Banner scanned the room seeing the faces of many he loved and those who supported him. He could feel the warmth and peace of the Holy Spirit telling him that he was on the proper course. He looked back into the camera, trying to picture the people who were watching from their homes. He tried to put the love he felt for each of them and his country in his voice as he ended his remarks.

"May God's guidance be with you and the United States of America, that we may have independence forever!"

PRESERVE, PROTECT & DEFEND

EPILOGUE

The future of America and our freedom depends on the actions of each of us today. There is a tendency to read history and think that the way things happened are the way they had to be, but the events we read in history could have gone a number of different directions. The history of Germany and the world could have been very different had Hitler and the Nazi Party been prevented from gaining power. England could have been lost to Hitler's Germany had it not been for the determination and optimism of Winston Churchill and others. JFK could have been a two-term President had the conspiracy to take his life been stopped.

The events of September 11, 2001, may have been much different had one ticket agent acted upon the promptings he received. Michael Tuohey, a ticket agent for US Airways in Portland, Maine, went to work at the airport like he had for 37 years, arriving at 4:30 on the morning of September 11.

"Tuohey was working the preferred customers' line, where the frequent travelers and high-end flyers get quick service. The line was empty... Then he spotted two young men come in and motioned them to his station."[170] At 5:40 a.m., Atta and Omari approached Tuohey's counter. Tuohey pulled up their information on the computer. They had one-way, first-class tickets to Los Angeles. The first leg of the flight was US Airways Flight 5930 from Portland, Maine, to Boston, and the second leg was American Airlines Flight 11, non-stop from Boston to Los Angeles. Tuohey noted that the flight left in 20 minutes and said to Atta, "You're cutting it close ... Got any bags?"[171] Atta checked two bags. "Tuohey then checked their drivers' licenses ... [and] his eyes locked on Atta... Then Tuohey went through an internal debate that still haunts him."[172]

Tuohey felt something was wrong. He recalled, "I got chills when I looked at [Atta]."[173] "I got an uncomfortable feeling... I said to myself, 'If this guy doesn't look like an Arab terrorist, then nothing does.'"[174] Tuohey had checked in thousands of Arabic people during the years, and never had such thoughts or feelings. However, Tuohey began to rationalize away his instincts. He gave himself a politically correct "mental slap, because in this day and age, it's not nice to say things like this."[175] The two men were wearing ties and jackets so he thought to himself, "These are just a couple of Arab businessmen."[176] "Setting aside his gut reaction, Tuohey issued the boarding passes."[177]

Atta and Omari arrived in Boston at 6:45 a.m. and boarded American Airline Flight 11 bound for Los Angeles. The plane took off at 7:59 a.m. and the hijacking began at 8:14 a.m. The terrorists stabbed flight attendants and passengers and controlled the others by spraying

Mace. The hijackers gained access to the cockpit, and Atta—the only terrorist on board trained to fly a jet—took control of the aircraft. At 8:26 a.m. the plane was "flying erratically," and a minute later, Flight 11 turned south.[178]

At 8:46 a.m. American Airlines Flight 11 "traveling at hundreds of miles per hour and carrying some 10,000 gallons of jet fuel plowed into the North Tower of the World Trade Center in Lower Manhattan. At 9:03, a second airliner hit the South Tower. Fire and smoke billowed upward. Steel, glass, ash, and bodies fell below. The Twin Towers, where up to 50,000 people worked each day, both collapsed less than 90 minutes later. . . More than 2,600 people died in the World Trade Center [attack]."[179]

Tuohey was told by a co-worker that American Airlines Flight 11 had crashed into the World Trade Center, and a few minutes later, he heard of the second crash. In response, Tuohey said, "I checked in two guys for the flight, and I thought they were terrorists."[180] He now knew his instincts had been correct saying, "I was right. This guy was a terrorist."[181]

Since 9/11, Tuohey has been "wracked by guilt at the thought he could have done something to stop it"[182] and on CNN he stated, "I felt ashamed that I did not react to my instincts."[183]

"Tuohey says he just hopes that the next person chosen by chance to make that first contact with evil . . . does what he did not, and reacts when his gut tells him to. [Tuohey stated,] 'I had the devil standing right in front of me, you know, and I ignored him.'"[184] If Tuohey had acted, the story may have had a much different ending. Following 9/11, Tuohey vehemently stated, "I will never ignore my instincts again." He "worked for three more years at the US Airways ticket counter before retiring... [and] twice his inquiries led to arrests."[185]

Today we are each writing history. America does not have to lose its freedom as a result of evil and corruption. The destiny of America will be determined by the actions of you and me. The battle between good and evil is before us each day. Will your children and grandchildren read about your actions and say, "My mom, dad, grandfather, or grandmother was a patriot that fought to preserve and restore the freedoms we enjoy"? If the freedoms of America are to be preserved and restored, it will be done by "We the People." It was an untrained, un-uniformed American army of farm boys that defeated the superior British forces.

I would like to share with you one final story from the Revolutionary War, which took place on December 31, 1776. A sergeant in the army recorded, "Our men . . . were without shoes or other comfortable clothing; and as traces of our march towards Princeton, the ground was literally marked with the blood of the soldier's feet. . . On the last day of December 1776 the time for which I and most of my regiment had enlisted expired [Washington called the regiment into formation and urged them to reenlist. The drums beat and Washington called for volunteers willing to stay to step forward]. Not a man turned out. The soldiers worn down with fatigue and privations, had their hearts fixed on home and the comforts of the domestic circle, and it was hard to forego the anticipated pleasures of the society of our dearest friends. [Washington turned and began to ride away, and then stopped].

"The General wheeled his horse about, rode in front of the regiment and addressing us again said, 'My brave fellows, you have done all I asked you to do, and more than could be reasonably expected, but your country is at stake, your wives, your houses, and all that you hold dear. You have worn yourselves out with fatigues and hardships, but we know not how to spare you. If you will consent to stay one month longer, you will render that service to the cause of liberty, and to your country, which you can probably never do under any other circumstance. The present is emphatically the crisis, which is to decide our destiny.' The drums beat a second time. The soldiers felt the force of the appeal. One said to another, 'I will remain if you will.' Others remarked 'We cannot go home under such circumstances.' A few stepped forth, and their example was immediately followed by nearly all."[186] "God Almighty inclined their hearts to listen to the proposal and they engaged anew. Let it be remembered to their Eternal honor."[187]

America is again faced with a crisis that will decide our destiny. You are needed to enlist in the cause for freedom. You have a unique opportunity to serve your country in the fight for freedom and be a part of the glorious cause of America. Your help is needed to teach and inspire others to learn and live the principles of freedom.

What Can You Do?

1. Share this book, *Preserve, Protect, and Defend*, with family, friends, neighbors, co-workers, church members, etc.
2. Complete the Patriots Training and encourage others to complete the Patriots Training. From this training, you will hear miraculous stories of God's hand in the settling of America and the building of this great nation. You will study the entire Constitution from

the viewpoint of the Founding Fathers. You will study the people, organizations, and groups who have been using their time, resources, and talents to change the direction of America in order to serve their own special self-interests. You will learn how the Constitution can be restored to its proper place in government. Learn more about this training at www.TheGloriousCauseOfAmerica.org

3. With other patriots, I have founded the non-profit organization, The Glorious Cause of America Institute. Our mission is to inspire America to preserve, protect, defend, and live the inspired principles of freedom found in the original Constitution of the United States. Your donations to the cause are needed. You can learn more at www.TheGloriousCauseOfAmerica.org

4. Become a volunteer for The Glorious Cause of America Institute. We are always looking for good volunteers to assist us in achieving our goals. Please send us an email with the time you can commit to the cause, specific skills, and tasks you have interest in. Send an email to Cameron@GloriousCause.org

5. Pick a day and time each week to teach and discuss the principles of freedom as a family.

6. Make sure the principles of freedom are taught in your local schools. Fight to have socialist views of history and government removed from the schools.

7. Fight to remove unconstitutional laws and leaders and promote and support constitutional laws and leaders.

8. Invite the author of this book or other constitutional scholars to speak to your church, school, association, or other organization. Learn more at www.TheGloriousCauseOfAmerica.org

A monk wrote more than nine hundred years ago, "When I was a young man, I wanted to change the world. I found it was difficult to change the world, so I tried to change my nation. When I found I couldn't change the nation, I began to focus on my town. I couldn't change the town and as an older man, I tried to change my family. Now, as an old man, I realize the only thing I can change is myself, and suddenly I realize that if long ago I had changed myself, I could have made an impact on my family. My family and I could have made an impact on our town. Their impact could have changed the nation, and I could indeed have changed the world."[188]

I enjoy hearing from readers. Please send me an email with your thoughts about the book.

CameronCTaylor@DoesYourBagHaveHoles.org

"Perseverance and spirit have done wonders in all ages."
General George Washington

About the Author

Cameron C. Taylor is a nationally recognized scholar who has been invited to present lectures and seminars to organizations all across the country. Cameron is the author of the books *Preserve, Protect, and Defend, Does Your Bag Have Holes? 24 Truths That Lead to Financial and Spiritual Freedom, 8 Attributes of Great Achievers*, and *Twelve Paradoxes of the Gospel*. Cameron's books have been endorsed by Ken Blanchard, co-author of *The One Minute Manager*, Dr. Stephen R. Covey, author of *The Seven Habits of Highly Effective People*, Billionaire Jon Huntsman, Sr., Rich DeVos, owner of the Orlando Magic, William Danko, PhD, co-author of *The Millionaire Next Door*, and many others. Cameron graduated with honors from business school and is the founder of several multimillion dollar companies. He is also a founder of The Glorious Cause of America Institute and serves on its board of directors. Cameron is a recipient of the Circle of Honor Award for being an "exceptional example of honor, integrity, and commitment." He lives in Idaho with his wife and three children. Cameron is a gifted teacher and presenter who has been invited to speak at hundreds of meetings with excellent reviews.

"Where the Spirit of the Lord is, there is liberty."
2 Corinthians 3:17

Acknowledgements

I would like to thank the many people who helped with the completion of this book. I would like to express individual thanks:

To Paula Taylor. I am greatly blessed to be married to Paula. She is a woman of many, many talents. She has played a key role in the writing and editing of each of my books. I appreciate her constant and enduring support.

To Melissa Bruce. Her talents as a writer greatly improved the quality of this work. I appreciate the many hours she spent with the initial manuscript to improve the characters, story, and dialogue.

To Natalie Kraus. I appreciate the time she took to edit the manuscripts from her perspective as a novelist. Her additions and changes improved the book.

To G.K. Mangelson. I appreciate his years of support and friendship. We have worked on many projects together including The Glorious Cause of America Institute. I appreciate his willingness to serve and be a champion of liberty.

To Lynell Shock. I appreciate her volunteering her time and proofreading skill to assist the cause. She has a gift.

To Jim Jones. I appreciate his efforts editing the book. Jim is a man of service and a man of many talents.

To Jessica Dyer and Catherine Christensen for their work as editors.

To Todd Thompson for the cover art and illustrations—he is a brilliant designer who is fantastic to work with.

Endnotes

1   Paul Schatzkin, *The Boy Who Invented Television* (Silver Spring, MD: Teamcom Books, 2002), 249.

2   From speech "The Glorious Cause of Freedom" delivered by David McCullough on September 27, 2005 at Brigham Young University in Provo, UT.

3   Cokie Roberts, *Founding Mothers* (New York, NY: HarperCollins Publishers, 2004), 97.

4   Victor Frankl, *Man's Search for Meaning* (Boston, MA: Beacon Press, 1959), 113.

5   Jared Sparks, *The Writing of George Washington, Volume II* (Boston: Russel, Osiorne, and Metcalf, 1834), 469-470.

6   David Barton, *The Bulletproof George Washington* (Aledo, TX: Wall Builders, 2003), 39.

7   Washington Irving, *Life of George Washington, Volume I* (New York: G. P. Putnam and Son, 1869), 218. Phrase from letter written by Washington to his brother John.

8   John Frederick, *Life and Times of Washington, Volume I* (Albany, NY: M. M. Belcher Publishing Co., 1903), 247-248.

9   John Warner Barber, *Thrilling Incidents in American History* (New York: James Miller, 1868), 90.

10 Samuel Kercheval, *A History of the Valley of Virginia* (Woodstock, VA: John Gatewood, 1850), 320.

11 Eugene Parsons, *George Washington: A Character Sketch* (Chicago: University Association, 1898), 30–31.

12 Ronald Reagan, *An American Life* (New York, NY: Simon & Schuster, 1990), 263. On March 30, 1981, Ronald Reagan was shot by John Hinckley, Jr.; Reagan became the first President to survive a gun shot wound from an assassination attempt. Reagan believed that God protected his life for a future mission he was to perform. After returning from the hospital to the White House, Reagan wrote in his diary, "I owe my life to God and will try to serve him in every way I can."

13 James Russell Lowell , *The Writings of James Russell Lowell, Vol. 6.*, (Boston and New York: Houghton, Mifflin and Co., 1893), 207. When James Russell Lowell, a nineteenth century American writer, was asked, "How long will the American Republic endure?" he replied: "As long as the ideas of the men who founded it continue dominant."

14 Benjamin Franklin, *The Works of Dr. Benjamin Franklin* (New York: W. Van Norden, 1825), 87.

15   Quote by Edward Everett. Jasper L. McBrien, *Twentieth Biennial Report of the State Superintendent of Public Instruction to the Governor of the State of Nebraska* (Nebraska. Dept. of Public Instruction, 1908), 399.

16   Thomas Jefferson, John P. Foley, *The Jeffersonian Cyclopedia* (London: Funk & Wagnalls Company, 1900), 605.

17   William J. Federer, *America's God and Country Encyclopedia of Quotations* (St. Louis, MO: Amerisearch, Inc, 2000), 392.

18   Kay Brigham, *Christopher Columbus: His Life and Discovery in the Light of His Prophecies* (Terrassa, Barcelona, Spain: CLIE Publishers, 1990), 170. Quote adapted from this actual quote, "At this time I have seen and put in study to look into all the Scriptures, cosmography, histories, chronicles and philosophy and other arts, which the Lord opened to my understanding (I could sense his hand upon me), so that it became clear to me that it was feasible to navigate from here to the Indies; and he unlocked within me the determination to execute this idea... Who doubts that this illumination was from the Holy Spirit? I attest that [the Spirit], with marvelous rays of light, consoled me through the holy and sacred Scriptures, a strong and clear testimony, with forty-four books of the Old Testament, and four Gospels with twenty-three Epistles of those blessed Apostles, encouraging me to proceed, and continually, without ceasing for a moment, they inflame me with a sense of great urgency... No one should be afraid to take on any enterprise in the name of our Saviour."

19   Jacob Wassermann, *Columbus, Don Quixote of the Seas* (Boston: Little, Brown and Co., 1930), 19–20.

20   Christopher Columbus' son Fernando quoted his father as saying of the discovery, "God gave me the faith, and afterwards the courage so that I was quite willing to undertake the journey."

21   Words written by Columbus in his ship log, October 11, 1492; Bill Halamandaris, *The Heart of America: Ten Core Values That Make Our Country Great*, Deerfield Beach, FL: Health Communications, Inc., 2004), 30.

22   Adapted from expert of the ship log abstract of October 10, 1492. "The men lost all patience... but the Admiral encouraged them in the best manner he could ... having come so far, they had nothing to do but continue on to the Indies, till with the help of our Lord, they should arrive there."

23   William D. Phillips, Jr. and Carla Rahn Phillips, *The Worlds of Christopher Columbus* (New York: Cambridge University Press, 1992), 152–153.

24   Christopher Columbus, *Personal Narrative of the First Voyage of Columbus to America* (Boston: Thomas B. Wait and Son, 1827), 240. Columbus wrote of name the first island, "I named the first of these islands San Salvador, thus bestowing upon it the name of our holy Saviour under whose protection I made the discovery." Today San Salvador Island is an island in the Bahamas and has a population of approximately about 1,000 and is home to the Club Med Columbus Isle resort.

25 Christopher Columbus, *Letter of Christopher Columbus to Rafael Sanchez* (Chicago: W.H. Lowdermilk Co., 1893), 13–14. Following Columbus' discovery of the Americas, he wrote a summary account of his voyage for King Ferdinand and Queen Isabella. It reads in part, "The great success of this enterprise is not to be ascribed to my own merits, but to . . . the Lord often granting to men what they never imagine themselves capable of effecting, as he is accustomed to hear the prayers of his servants and those who love his commandments, even in that which appears impossible; in this manner has it happened to me who have succeeded in an undertaking never before accomplished by man. . . And now ought the king, queen, princes, and all their dominions, as well as the whole of Christians, to give thanks to our Saviour Jesus Christ who has granted us such a victory and great success."

26 John Marshall, *The Life of George Washington, Volume II* (London: Richard Phillips, 1804), 424.

27 Benjamin Franklin Thompson, *History of Long Island* (New York: E. French, 1839), 360.

28 Benjamin Franklin Thompson, *History of Long Island* (New York: E. French, 1839), 360.

29 Edwin Burrows, *Forgotten Patriots: The Untold Story of American Prisoners During the Revolutionary War* (New York: Basic Books: 2008), 22.

30 W.T.R. Saffell, *Records of the Revolutionary War* (Baltimore: Charles C. Saffell, 1894), 304-306.

31 Edwin Burrows, *Forgotten Patriots: The Untold Story of American Prisoners During the Revolutionary War* (New York: Basic Books, 2008).

32 Retrieved November 7, 2008 from http://www.longislandgenealogy.com/prison.html.

33 W.T.R. Saffell, *Records of the Revolutionary War* (Baltimore: Charles C. Saffell, 1894), 307.

34 W.T.R. Saffell, *Records of the Revolutionary War* (Baltimore: Charles C. Saffell, 1894), 323.

35 On June 16th in response to the request that he accept the appointment as general, George Washington said, "Mr. President . . . I feel great distress . . . that my abilities and military experience may not be equal to the extensive and important trust. However, as the Congress desire it, I will enter upon the momentous duty, and exert every power I possess in their service, and for support of the glorious cause."

36 Jared Sparks, *The Writings of George Washington, Volume IV* (Boston: Ferdinand Andrews, 1838), 37-38.

37 Constitution of the United States, Article 6, Section 2.

38 Glenn Beck with Joshua Charles, *The Original Argument* (New York, NY: Threshold Editions, 2011), XXVII-XXVIII.

39 John Quincy Adams, *An Eulogy on the Life and Character of James Madison* (Boston, MA: Amercan Stationers' Company, 1836), 4, 85.

40 Benjamin Franklin, *The Works of Benjamin Franklin, Volume XI* (New York and London: G. P. Putnam's Sons, The Knickerbocker Press, 1904), 377.

41 E. H. Scott (Editor), *James Madison, Journal of the Federal Convention* (Chicago: Scott, Foresman and Co., 1898), 741-743.

42 George Ticknor Curtis, *Constitutional History of the United States, Volume I* (New York: Harper & Brothers, Franklin Square, 1889), 294.

43 James Madison, *The Papers of James Madison, Volume II* (Washington: Langtree & O'Sullivan, 1840), 718–719.

44 *A Collection of Essays by Alexander Hamilton John Jay and James Madison Interpreting the Constitution of the United States and Agreed Upon by the Federal Convention, September 17, 1787* (New York: The Colonial Press, 1901), 195.

45 Paul Leicester Ford, *Essays on the Constitution of the United States* (Brooklyn, NY: Historical Printing Club, 1892), 288.

46 Paul Leicester Ford, *Essays on the Constitution of the United States* (Brooklyn, NY: Historical Printing Club, 1892), 412.

47 Thomas Jefferson, John P. Foley (Editor), *The Jeffersonian Cyclopedia* (New York and London: Funk & Wagnalls Company, 1900), v, 153.

48 United States Declaration of Independence.

49 Ayn Rand, *Capitalism* (New York: Signet, 1967), 325.

50 Seven social sins identified by Gandhi are wealth without work, pleasure without conscience, knowledge without character, commerce without morality, science without humanity, religion without sacrifice, and politics without principle.

51 "Fable of the Gullible Gull," *Reader's Digest*, October 1950, p. 32.

52 C.S. Lewis, *The Problem of Pain* (New York: HarperCollins, 2001), 25.

53 David Barton, "The Separation of Church and State," *WallBuilders*, Retrieved May 5, 2011 from http://www.wallbuilders.com/LIBissuesArticles. asp?id=123.

54 United States Constitution, Bill of Rights, Amendment I.

55 President Dwight Eisenhower in a message to the Knights of Columbus at a meeting held in Louisville, KY, on August 17, 1954.

56 Melvin Ballard, Jr., "Religion in a Free Society," lecture delivered July 5, 1992, at America's Freedom Festival.

57 Engel v. Board of Education, 330 US 1, 18 (1947); Abington v. Schempp, 374 US 421 (1962); Commissioner of Education v. School Committee of Leyden, 267 N.E. 2d 226 (Mass. 1971), cert. denied, 404 US 849.

58 Stone v. Graham, 449 US 39 (1980); Ring v. Grand Forks Public School District, 483 F. Sup. 272 (D.C. ND 1980); Lanner v. Wimmer, 662 F. 2d 1349 (10th Cir. 1991).

59 McCreary County v. American Civil Liberties Union; Forced removal of Ten Commandments display from the McCreary County, KY, courthouse.

60 Warsaw v. Tehachapi, CV F-90-404 EDP (E.D. Ca. 1990).

61 Roberts v. Madigan, 702 F. Supp. 1505 (D. Colo. 1989), 921 F. 2d 1047 (10th Cir. 1990), cert. denied, 505 US 1218 (1992).

62 Allegheny v. American Civil Liberties Union, 492 US 573, 614 (1989).

63 Iverson v. Forbes, 93-3-232 (Or. Cir. Ct. 1993).

64 Reidenback v. Pethtel, 3:93CV632 (E.D. Va. 1993).

65 Bebout v. Leimbaugh, 93-C-1079 J (C.D. Ut. 1993).

66 David Barton, *Original Intent* (Aledo, TX: Wallbuilder Press, 2000), 16.

67 Russ Miller, Jim Dobkins, *The Theft of America's Heritage* (Phoenix, AZ: UCS Press, 2008), 37.

68 Ezra Benson, United States Secretary of Agriculture from January 21, 1953 to January 20, 1961.

69 B. L. Rayner, *Life of Thomas Jefferson* (Boston: Lilly, Wait, Colman & Holden, 1834), 37.

70 Thomas Jefferson, Albert Ellery Bergh, *The Writings of Thomas Jefferson, Volume III* (Washington, D.C.: Thomas Jefferson Memorial Association, 1903), 320–321.

71 Description of John Adams by Thomas Jefferson in a letter to Doctor Benjamin Rush on January 16, 1811. Thomas Jefferson, *The Writings of Thomas Jefferson, Volume IX* (New York, NY: G.P. Putnam's Sons, 1898), 296.

72 Description of John Adams by Thomas Jefferson in a letter to James Madison on August 30, 1823. Thomas Jefferson, *The Writing of Thomas Jefferson, Volume VII* (New York, NY: Derby & Jackson, 1859), 305.

73 Helen Ainslie Smith, *One Hundred Famous Americans* (New York: George Routledge and Sons, 1886), 58.

74 David McCullough, *John Adams* (New York, NY: Touchstone, 2001), 645.

75 B.J Losing, *Signers of the Declaration of Independence* (New York: George F. Colledge & Brother, 1848), 182.

76 David McCullough, *John Adams* (New York, NY: Touchstone, 2001), 647.

77 Description of Thomas Jefferson by Abigail Adams. Cokie Roberts, *Ladies of Liberty* (New York, NY: HarperCollins Publishers, 2008), 259.

78 Letter written by John Adams to Thomas Jefferson on March 1, 1787. John Adams, *The Works of John Adams, Vol. VIII* (Boston, MA: Little, Brown and Company, 1853), 435.

79 Massachusetts Constitution of 1780 Article 1.

80 Charles Hockema.

81 Bruce Smith, *Liberty and Liberalism* (London: Longmans, Green and Co., 1887), 430.

82 Donald S. Lutz, *The Origins of American Constitutionalism* (Baton Rouge, LA: Louisiana State University Press, 1988), 140–142. To find out which resources the Founding Fathers drew upon during the founding period, a study was performed that examined the citations in public political literature

written between 1760 and 1805. The most frequently cited book in the sample literature was the Bible with 34 percent of the citations. Other major sources of the citations were Montesquieu, a French writer famous for his theory on the separation of powers, with 8.3 percent; William Blackstone, an English jurist and professor who wrote the book Commentaries on the Laws of England, with 7.9 percent; and John Locke, an English philosopher who developed the concepts of "government with the consent of the governed" and "rights of life, liberty, and property," with 2.9 percent.

83 John Adams, Charles Francis Adams, *The Works of John Adams, Volume IV* (Boston: Little, Brown and Company, 1854), 229.

84 Ezra Benson, United States Secretary of Agriculture from January 21, 1953 to January 20, 1961.

85 Attributed to Alexis de Tocqueville but not found in his works.

86 From John Adams notes for a lecture at Braintree, MA in the Spring 1772.

87 David Crockett, *Life of Col. David Crockett* (Philadelphia: G.G. Evans, 1860), 20–21.

88 Oath of Office in place in 1826 was "'I do solemnly swear that I will support the Constitution of the United States." The current oath taken by congressman is, "I do solemnly swear (or affirm) that I will support and defend the Constitution of the United States against all enemies, foreign and domestic; that I will bear true faith and allegiance to the same; that I take this obligation freely, without any mental reservation or purpose of evasion; and that I will well and faithfully discharge the duties of the office on which I am about to enter: So help me God."

89 Nathaniel Wright Stephenson, *Texas and the Mexican War* (New Haven: Yale University Press, 1921), 71.

90 The inscription on Davy Crockett's tombstone reads, "Davy Crockett, Pioneer, Patriot, Soldier, Trapper, Explorer, State Legislator, Congressman, Martyred at The Alamo. 1786–1836".

91 Edward S. Ellis, *The Life of Colonel David Crockett* (Philadelphia: Poter & Coates, 1884), 138–148.

92 Jonathan Elliot, James Madison, *The Debates in the Several State Conventions on the Adoption of the Federal Constitution, Volume IV* (Washington, DC, Taylor & Maury, 1863), 429.

93 Frederic Bastiat, *The Law* (Whitefish, MT: Kessinger Publishing, 2004), 21. The Law was originally published as a pamphlet in 1850.

94 Frederic Bastiat, *The Law* (Whitefish, MT: Kessinger Publishing, 2004), 18, 14. The Law was originally published as a pamphlet in 1850.

95 Frederic Bastiat, *The Law* (Whitefish, MT: Kessinger Publishing, 2004), 8. The Law was originally published as a pamphlet in 1850.

96 Alabama Constitution, Article 1, Section 35.

97 S. E. (Samuel Eagle) Forman, *The Life and Writings of Thomas Jefferson* (Indianapolis: The Bowen-Merrill Company, 1900), 408–409.

98 Upton Sinclair, Jack London, *The Cry for Justice* (New York: Upton Sinclair, 1915), 305.

99 From speech delivered by Woodrow Wilson, 28th President of the United States, on May 9, 1912.

100 *PBS*, retrieved 9-24-2009 from http://www.pbs.org/benfranklin/l3_citizen_founding.html.

101 Introductory Note, Benjamin Franklin, *The Autobiography of Benjamin Franklin* (Dover Publications, Inc., 1996), iii.

102 Henry S. Randall, *The Life of Thomas Jefferson, Volume III* (New York: Derby & Jackson, 1858), 648. S.E. Forman, *The Life and Writings of Thomas Jefferson* (Indianapolis: Bowen–Merrill Company, 1900), 159.

103 Jay Van Andel, *An Enterprising Life* (New York: Harper Collins, 1998), 162.

104 Winston Churchill.

105 A study of the 4,047 American millionaires in 1892 found that 84 percent became millionaires without the benefit of inherited wealth. Stanley Lebergott, *The American Economy* (Princeton, NJ: Princeton University Press, 1976), 169–170. $1 million dollars in 1892 is the equivalent of $21 million dollars in 2006.

106 In 1996, approximately 3.5 million households in America (out of a total of 100 million households) had a net worth of $1 million or more [and] ... fewer than 20 percent inherited 10 percent or more of their wealth. Thomas J. Stanley, William D. Danko, *The Millionaire Next Door* (New York: Simon & Schuster, 1996), 212, 16.

107 J. Willard Marriott, founder of Marriott International.

108 The bottom twenty percent of income earners in the US performed 4.3 percent of all the work in the US economy, while those in the top twenty percent of income earners performed 33.8 percent. Thus, the top quintile performed almost eight times as much labor as did the bottom quintile. Robert Rector and Rea Hederman, Jr., "Two Americas: One Rich, One Poor? Understanding Income Inequality in the United States," August 24, 2004.

109 Edited by E. Boyd Smith, Benjamin Franklin, *The Autobiography of Benjamin Franklin* (New York: Henry Holt and Company, 1916), 113.

110 Walter Isaacson, *Benjamin Franklin* (New York: Simon & Schuster, 2003), 72.

111 US Department of Treasury, Office of Tax Analysis, "Household Income Mobility During the 1980s: A Statistical Assessment Based on Tax Return Data," June 1, 1992. Isabel Sawhill and Mark Condon, "Is US Inequality Really Growing?", *Policy Bites*, June 1992, Washington, D.C., cited in US Department of Treasury, Office of Tax Analysis, "Household Income Mobility During the 1980s: A Statistical Assessment Based on Tax Return Data," June 1, 1992.

A study was done by the US Treasury Department to determine if, over time, Americans move from one income class to another. The study analyzed a random sample of 14,351 tax returns from 1979 to 1988. This sample was broken into five groups based on income in 1979 with the lowest 20 percent of income earners in the 1st group and the top 20 percent of income earners in the 5th group. In 1988, the 14,351 tax returnee's income was again analyzed. During the 10-year period, 86 percent of the lowest income earners had increased their income and moved to a higher earning group. In addition, more of the lowest income earners (1st group) who became the highest income earners (5th group) than remained in the lowest group (see table). During this 10 year study, the poor did not get poorer; they got richer and became the rich. Those now considered rich were at one point in their lives the poor. For most people poverty is temporary. Even those who choose to stay poor still get richer as the economy grows.

America on the Move

1979 Group	1st	2nd	3rd	4th	5th
	\multicolumn{5}{c}{Percent in Each Group in 1988}
1st (Lowest 20%)	14.2%	20.7%	25.0%	25.3%	14.7%
2nd	10.9%	29.0%	29.6%	19.5%	11.1%
3rd (Middle 20%)	5.7%	14.0%	33.0%	32.3%	15.0%
4th	3.1%	9.3%	14.8%	37.5%	35.4%
5th (Highest 20%)	1.1%	4.4%	9.4%	20.3%	64.7%

The Urban Institute did a similar study from 1977 to 1986. They found that during the ten-year period, the income of the bottom fifth of income earners increased by 77 percent ($12,145) while the income of the top 20 percent of income earners increased by 5 percent ($4,609) (see table). The poor are not getting poorer. From this study, you could say the rich get a little richer and the poor get a lot richer.

Average Family Income (in constant 1991 dollars)

Group	Average Family Income 1977	1986	Change in Avg Family Income Amount	Percent
1st (Lowest 20%)	$15,853	$27,998	$12,145	77%
2nd	$31,340	$43,041	$11,701	37%
3rd (Middle 20%)	$43,297	$51,796	$8,499	20%
4th	$57,486	$63,314	$5,828	10%
5th (Highest 20%)	$92,531	$97,140	$4,609	5%

The myth the rich gets richer and the poor get poorer is perpetuated by flawed studies, data, and reports. For example, during the same time period of the Urban Institute study, according to the census data, the income of the bottom fifth of families declined 2.8 percent and the average income of the top fifth rose 16.4 percent. (Cited in: Dick Armey, Joint Economic Committee, "Family Income Growth and Income Equality: Progress or Punishment?", July 1992) This data is inaccurate because it is comparing two samples of income earners which do not consist of the same people. The US Treasury Department found that the median age of the 1st quintile was 21, rising to age 37 in the 3rd and reaching age 61 in the 90th percentile. (US Department of Treasury, Office of Tax Analysis, "Household Income Mobility During the 1980s: A Statistical Assessment Based on Tax Return Data," June 1, 1992) So the census data in 1977 of the bottom income earners would include people who on average were 21 years of age and the comparison sample ten years later from the census data of the bottom income earners would include people who were on average 11 years old at the time of the first sample who were now on average 21 years old and earning income. To draw conclusion about the income of bottom income earners on such census data would be like a college analyzing how much its graduated students are making by sampling the current students. To get accurate data you have to follow the same group of people over time, which is what the US Treasury Department and Urban Institute studies did.

112 Abraham Lincoln, *Life and Works of Abraham Lincoln, Volume V* (New York: The Current Literature Publishing Co., 1907), 67–68, 186.

113 Genesis 1:20–21, 28; Genesis 9:7.

114 Stephen R. Covey, *Principle-Centered Leadership* (New York: Simon & Schuster, 1991), 159.

115 Stephen Budiansky, "10 Billion for Dinner, Please," *US News & World Report*, 12 September 1994, p. 57–62

116 Paul Pilzer, *God Wants You to Be Rich* (New York: Simon & Schuster, 1995) p. 18–19.

117 US Census Bureau.

118 World Bank, World Development Indicators Database, Table: Total GDP 2005, July 1, 2006.

119 Stanley Lebergott, *The American Economy* (Princeton, NJ: Princeton University Press, 1976), 164.

120 Ezra Benson, United States Secretary of Agriculture from January 21, 1953 to January 20, 1961.

121 Oliver J. Thatcher, *The Library of Original Sources, Volume X* (New York: University Research Extension, 1907), 29.

122 Anyone who tells you the rich don't pay taxes because they use loopholes in the tax system hasn't looked at the facts. In 2002, the top 10 percent of income earners paid more than 67 percent of all federal income tax while the bottom

40 percent received more in welfare than they contribute in federal income taxes (see table).

Share of Federal Tax Liabilities, 2002

Income Category	% of Federal Income Taxes Paid
Lowest Quintile	-2.6%
Second Quintile	-0.2%
Middle Quintile	5.3%
Fourth Quintile	14.8%
Highest Quintile	82.8%
Top 10%	67.4%

123 Thomas Jefferson, Albert Ellery Bergh, *The Writings of Thomas Jefferson*, Volume III (Washington, D.C.: Thomas Jefferson Memorial Association, 1903), 320–321.

124 Thomas Jefferson, *The Writings of Thomas Jefferson, Volume VI* (New York: Derby & Jackson, 1859), 574–575.

125 Ayn Rand, *Capitalism* (New York: Signet, 1967), 100–101. Words of Alan Greenspan, chairman of the Board of Governors of the Federal Reserve of the United States from 1987–2006.

126 Ezra Benson, United States Secretary of Agriculture from 1953–1961.

127 W. Cleon Skousen, *The Cleansing of America* (Riverton, UT: Ensign Publishing, 2010), 85, 96.

128 B.F. Morris, *Memorial Record of the Nation's Tribute to Abraham Lincoln* (Washington, DC: W. H. & O. H. Morrison, 1865), 267.

129 Winston Churchill, *The Second World War, Volume I, The Gathering Storm* (New York: Houghton Mifflin Company, 1948), 601. Winston Churchill reflection on May 10th, 1940 when he took office as Prime Minister of England.

130 Alonzo Rothschild, *Honest Abe* (Boston and New York: Houghton Mifflin Company, 1917), 222-224.

131 Abraham Lincoln, Charles W. Moores (Editor), *Lincoln Addresses and Letters* (New York: American Book Company, 1914).

132 From speech "The Glorious Cause of Freedom" delivered by David McCullough on September 27, 2005 at Brigham Young University in Provo, UT.

133 Ida Minerva Tarbell, *The Life of Abraham Lincoln, Volume II* (New York: The Macmillan Company, 1917), 125.

134 Booker T. Washington, *Up From Slavery* (New York: Doubleday, Page & Co., 1907), 19-21.

135 Abraham Lincoln, James Baird McClure, *Abraham Lincoln's Stories and Speeches* (Chicago: Rhodes & McClure Publishing Company, 1906), 185-186.

136 B. J. Losing, *Signers of the Declaration of Independence* (New York: George F. Colledge & Brother, 1848), 167.

137 Benjamin Franklin, *Memoirs of Benjamin Franklin, Volume I* (Philadelphia: McCarty & Davis, 1834), 57.

138 Jared Sparks, *The Writing of George Washington, Volume II* (Boston: Russel, Osiorne, and Metcalf, 1834), 468.

139 The sash Washington received from General Braddock is in Mount Vernon's collection but is not currently on view. In recent years, the sash has been in several traveling exhibitions including, "George Washington: The Man Behind the Myths" and "Treasures from Mount Vernon." Because the sash was on view for a long period of time and is in delicate condition, Mount Vernon has restricted it from display for a number of years. Textiles are particularly vulnerable to light damage and can only be on exhibit for brief periods (a general rule that many museums follow is an item made of silk—like Braddock's sash—should only be on view 3 months for every 10 years). In order to protect the sash for future generations it is currently being stored in low light conditions.

140 Ronald Reagan, *An American Life* (New York, NY: Simon & Schuster, 1990), Dedication, Acknowledgements, 261.

141 Ronald Reagan, *An American Life* (New York: NY: Simon & Schuster, 1990), 263.

142 C.S. Lewis, *The Screwtape Letters* (New York: NY: HarperCollins, 2001), 61.

143 John 8:32, King James Version.

144 Genesis 5:16, Inspired Version.

145 Gary Allen, Larry Abraham, *None Dare Call It Conspiracy* (Cutchogue, NY: Buccaneer Books), 22.

146 2 Chronicles 7:14, New International Version.

147 The ceremony for George Washington's swearing in as the first President took place in the open outside gallery of the old City Hall in the presence of both Houses of Congress and a vast multitude of citizens. He was dressed in a plain suit of dark-brown cloth and white silk stockings, all of American manufacture. He never wore a wig. His ample hair was powdered and dressed in the fashion of the day, clubbed and ribboned. Robert Livingston administered the oath of office and Secretary of State, Samuel Otis, held the open Bible. After taking the oath and kissing the sacred volume on which he had laid his hands, he reverently closed his eyes, and in an attitude of devotion said, "So help me, God!" Livingston then said, "It is done!" And turning to the people, he shouted, "Long live George Washington, the first President of the United States." The shout was echoes and re-echoed by the populace. Washington and the members of Congress retired to the Senate chamber, where the President

delivered a most impressive inaugural address. Then he and the members went in procession to St. Paul's Chapel, and there invoked the blessings of Almighty God upon the new government. Benson John Lossing, Woodrow Wilson, *Harper's Encyclopedia of United States History from 458 A.D. to 1909, Volume 10* (New York, NY: Harper & Brothers Publishers, 1905), 226-227.

148 Sterling W. Sill, Dan McCormick, *Lessons from Great Lives* (Aylesbury Publishing, 2007), 31.

149 Celia Sandys, Jonathan Littman, *We Shall Not Fail* (New York: Portfolio, 2003), 3.

150 Winston Churchill, *The Second World War, Volume I, The Gathering Storm* (New York: Houghton Mifflin Company, 1948), 601.

151 Winston Churchill, *The Second World War, Volume II, Their Finest Hour* (New York: Houghton Mifflin Company, 1949), 24.

152 Winston Churchill, *The Second World War, Volume III, The Grand Alliance* (New York: Houghton Mifflin Company, 1950), 332.

153 Winston Spencer Churchill, *Never Give In! The Best of Winston Churchill's Speeches* (New York, Hyperion, 2003), 389-390.

154 Hyrum W. Smith, *What Matters Most* (New York: Simon & Schuster, 2000), 33-37.

155 Jared Sparks, *The Writings of George Washington, Volume IV* (Boston: Ferdinand Andrews, 1838), 38.

156 *Orations of American Orators* (New York: Colonial Press, 1900), 59.

157 Martin Luther King, Jr.

158 From speech "The Glorious Cause of Freedom" delivered by David McCullough on September 27, 2005 at Brigham Young University in Provo, UT.

159 Randy Howe, John Adams, *The Quotable John Adams* (Guilford, CT: Globe Prequot Press, 2008), 143.

160 Luke 16:10 Good News Translation.

161 From speech "The Glorious Cause of Freedom" delivered by David McCullough on September 27, 2005 at Brigham Young University in Provo, UT.

162 Michael Novak, Jana Novak, *Washington's God* (Cambridge, MA: Perseus Books, 2007), 4-5.

163 Letter from George Washington to the Inhabitants of Princeton on August 25, 1783. Editor President F.L. Patton, *The Princeton University Bulletin, Volumes IX to XII* (Princeton, NJ: Princeton University Press, 1901), 55.

164 *Orations of American Orators*, (New York: Colonial Press, 1900), 249–250

165 Washington's daughter, Nelly Custis–Lewis, wrote in a letter dated February 26, 1833 that her father's mottos were, "Deeds, not words" and "For God and my country"; Jared Sparks, *The Writings of George Washington, Volume XII*, (Boston: American Stationers' Company, 1837), 407.

166 Matthew 23:11, King James Version.

167 Remarks from President Ronald Reagan at Ecumenical Prayer Breakfast in Dallas, TX August 23, 1984. United States, Office of the Federal Register, *Ronald Reagan, Volume 11* (Government Printing Office, 1982), 113-114.

168 After the resignation of Richard Nixon, Gerald Ford said the following in his remarks after taking the oath of office as President, "I am acutely aware that you have not elected me as your President by your ballots, and so I ask you to confirm me as your President with your prayers."

169 Psalm 27:3 Revised Standard Version, Ephesians 6:10, King James Version.

170 David Hench, "Ticket Agent Haunted by Brush with 9/11 Hijackers," *The Portland Press Herald*, March 6, 2005.

171 David Hench, "Ticket Agent Haunted by Brush with 9/11 Hijackers," *The Portland Press Herald*, March 6, 2005.

172 David Hench, "Ticket Agent Haunted by Brush with 9/11 Hijackers," *The Portland Press Herald*, March 6, 2005.

173 September 11, 2005, "I Was the One," The Oprah Winfrey Show, Harpo Productions, Inc.

174 David Hench, "Ticket Agent Haunted by Brush with 9/11 Hijackers," *The Portland Press Herald*, March 6, 2005.

175 David Hench, "Ticket Agent Haunted by Brush with 9/11 Hijackers," *The Portland Press Herald*, March 6, 2005.

176 September 11, 2005, "I Was the One," The Oprah Winfrey Show, Harpo Productions, Inc.

177 Drew Griffin (CNN Correspondent), March 3, 2006, "Airline Worker Remembers Gut Feelings of 9/11," CNN.

178 The National Commission on Terrorist Attacks Upon the United States, *The 9/11 Commission Report*, (Washington, D.C.: Government Printing Office, 2004), 1–6.

179 The National Commission on Terrorist Attacks Upon the United States, *The 9/11 Commission Report*, Executive Summary, (Washington, D.C.: Government Printing Office, 2004), 1.

180 David Hench, "Ticket Agent Haunted by Brush with 9/11 Hijackers," *The Portland Press Herald*, March 6, 2005.

181 September 11, 2005, "I Was the One," The Oprah Winfrey Show, Harpo Productions, Inc.

182 David Hench, "Ticket Agent Haunted by Brush with 9/11 Hijackers," *The Portland Press Herald*, March 6, 2005.

183 Drew Griffin (CNN Correspondent), March 3, 2006, "Airline Worker Remembers Gut Feelings of 9/11," CNN.

184 Drew Griffin (CNN Correspondent), March 3, 2006, "Airline Worker Remembers Gut Feelings of 9/11," CNN.

185 David Hench, "Ticket Agent Haunted by Brush with 9/11 Hijackers," *The Portland Press Herald*, March 6, 2005.

186 *The Pennsylvania Magazine of History and Biography, Volume 20* (Philadelphia, PA, Historical Society of Pennsylvania, 1896), 515-516.

187 Gerald M. Carbone, *Nathanael Greene: A Biography of the American Revolution* (New York, NY: Palgrave Macmillan, 2008), 58.

188 Don Soderquist, *Live Learn Lead to Make a Difference* (Nashville, TN: J. Countryman, 2006), 9.

8 Attributes of Great Achievers

By Cameron C. Taylor

This book is filled with inspiring stories from the lives of great achievers past and present including Gandhi, the Wright Brothers, Abraham Lincoln, Winston Churchill, Walt Disney, Sam Walton, Jon Huntsman, Warren Buffet, Christopher Columbus, George Washington, Benjamin Franklin, and others. From this book, you will learn:

- How Winston Churchill's optimism enabled England to withstand the attacks of Hitler and eventually win the war.

- How Walt Disney used the power of goals to create (Snow White, Disneyland, etc.) and make his dreams come true.

- Why George Washington carried a bloody sash with him throughout his life.

- Powerful experiences from the Wright Brothers on taking the initiative.

- Stories on honesty from billionaire Jon Huntsman that illustrate nice guys really can, and do, finish first in life.

- Fifteen principles to build strong, uplifting relationships.

- How a World War II concentration camp prisoner was able to remain strong, happy, and peaceful even in the worst of environments.

- How Gandhi's "experiment with truth" enabled him to go from a shy boy and an average man, to the leader of 500 million people who called him "The Great Soul."

- How top CEOs use the principle of abundance to increase productivity and profits.
- Inspiring stories on persistence and overcoming failures from the Wright Brothers, Columbus, Sam Walton, Sylvester Stallone, Colonel Sanders, and the lives of other great achievers.

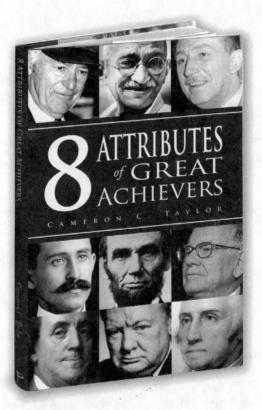

www.DoesYourBagHaveHoles.org

Does Your Bag Have Holes?
24 Truths That Lead to Financial and Spiritual Freedom
By Cameron C. Taylor

<u>Book Review by Joi Sigers</u>

Does Your Bag Have Holes? is what can only be called a perfect book. The lessons, ideals, illustrations, and quotes in this book have the power to change every single aspect of the reader's life for the better. What Cameron gives his readers in *Does Your Bag Have Holes?* is unique. The book contains information that you will not find anywhere else. It's a book that you'll find yourself returning to again and again and again. It's a book you won't just read, you'll experience it.

The world would be a much better place if Cameron C. Taylor wrote more books! Not only is he a fantastic author, he's a great teacher and motivator. I love to see someone doing what they were meant to do. There's a certain beauty about it. Whether it's Faith Hill singing, Frank Sinatra dancing, or Serena Williams playing tennis— there's something awe-inspiring when someone has found what they were meant to do, and they carry it out as beautifully as nature knew they would. Cameron was meant to write, and he does so beautifully. He writes with humor, insight, and profound wisdom.

I took countless notes while reading the book and his teachings have had a great impact upon my life. I came across so many different stories (with illustrations) that I wanted to scan/type in and send to the people on my e-mail list. They're that amazing. Then I realized, after I lost count of the number of stories, that it would be much wiser to simply shoot out one widespread e-mail recommending this book and everything in it. I've recommended this book to everyone I know and now would like to recommend it to you!

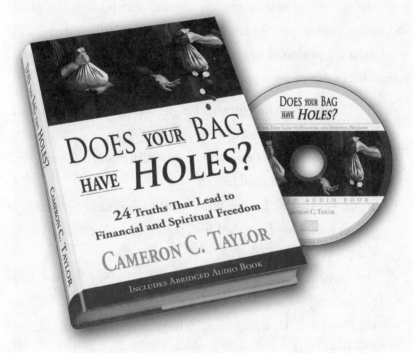

www.DoesYourBagHaveHoles.org

Twelve Paradoxes of the Gospel
By Cameron C. Taylor

The gospel of Jesus Christ is filled with paradoxes. Many of God's directions appear to be contrary to logic and reason. On the surface they appear to have the opposite effect of the promised result. This book explores twelve of these gospel paradoxes with powerful scriptures and stories from the lives of faith-filled Christians. In these paradoxical statements are profound truths that lead to happiness in this life and eternal life in the world to come.

- The Paradox of Faith contains insight on faith from the Apostle Peter's experience walking on water with Jesus.

- From the Paradox of Performance you will learn why the first shall be last; and the last shall be first.

- In the Paradox of Leadership you will read inspiring stories of servant leadership from the life of Jesus Christ, Abraham Lincoln, and the Founding Fathers.

- The Paradox of Wisdom contains three lessons learned from Balaam's talking donkey found in the book of Numbers.

- The Paradox of Receiving contains insights on prayer and receiving gifts from God.

- The Paradox of Pain answers the question of why bad things happen to good people.

- The Paradox of Forgiveness contains great stories from the life of Leonardo Da Vinci and others on the power of forgiveness.

- The Paradox of Wealth teaches principles every parent must know to raise productive, self-sufficient children and grandchildren.
- The Paradox of Giving shows how giving actually makes you richer.
- The Paradox of Fundamentals teaches how to apply in your life the formula legendary coach John Wooden used to create ten national championship teams in twelve years.

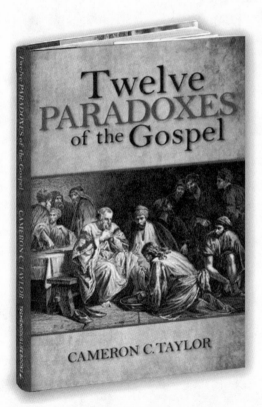

www.DoesYourBagHaveHoles.org